BECOMING A SERVANT-LEADER

a workbook
for bringing skill & spirit to professional & personal life

D1103987

Rayna Schroeder

Jackie Bahn-Henkelman, Ph.D

Jim Henkelman-Bahn, Ph.D

Originally published in three volumes as *Leading With Skill and Spirit: The Servant-Leader Journey*

ISBN 978-0-9754643-4-2

Graphic design and layout by Nathaniel Elberfeld & Alexandra Waller

Published by The Gabriel Center for Servant-Leadership
123 Church Street, NE Suite 150
Marietta, GA 30060
(678) 213-2750
www.gabrielcenter.org

To Jim and Cathy Fort, servant-leaders both.

| CONTENTS

foreword

by Quincy D. Brown

I have had the good fortune of knowing the work of the Gabriel Center for Servant-Leadership for over a decade through my work with students as chaplain and now as Vice President for Spiritual Life and Church Relations. Throughout the years, I have selected their *Leading with Skill and Spirit* manuals to enhance the education of our Servant-Leader Fellows, the student servant-leadership group that I advise at LaGrange College, to help our students make a difference in the world.

In the spring of 2012, Mark Elberfeld and Katie Elberfeld facilitated our annual Servant-Fellows Retreat at Callaway Gardens in Georgia utilizing many of the exercises in this book to help our group focus on the power of reflection, define servant-leadership, and group activities to develop intrapersonal and interpersonal awareness skills. Through these encounters, I have come to know the Gabriel Center best and to admire, exceedingly, their commitment to servant-leadership. Over the summer of 2012, I was asked to serve on the Gabriel Center's Board of Directors.

While using some of resources from *Leading with Skill and Spirit*, our Servant-Leader students began Panther Toy Store, a student-led initiative that raises funds to purchase toys as a "hand-up" instead of a handout to underprivileged families in the LaGrange/Troup County. In addition, our students began the Bus Project, where students submitted grant proposals to retrofit a school bus with school curriculum to become a mentoring/tutoring program on wheels. Through these and several other servant-leadership projects over that span of ten years, our students discovered that servant-leadership requires students to set aside personal gain, to make sacrifices, and to put the needs of others above the direction that they prefer for themselves. Through discovering their own passions, and following examples of other servant-leaders, our students understand that servant-leadership is not a particular style of leadership, but rather relates to the motivation behind a leader's thoughts, words and actions. Much of what the LaGrange College students gained originated with the help of the Gabriel Center learning tools.

Using concepts from different leadership theories and organizational practices to build a case for the importance of servant-leadership, this new edition from the Gabriel Center combines the three original volumes of *Leading with Skill and Spirit* into one. *Becoming a Servant-Leader* offers a conversation on what it means to be a servant-leader, one who leads by serving others. By highlighting the importance of personal awareness and interpersonal relationships, *Becoming a Servant-Leader* presents ideas and concepts on servant-leadership which are followed by an opportunity for reflection to provide the reader with real life examples of servant-leadership.

Based on experiential learning, *Becoming a Servant-Leader* is designed so that individuals and groups can direct themselves in the process of what it means for a leader to integrate personal strengths and weaknesses in order to lead by serving others. It is a commitment to service first — making other people's needs the highest priority. In doing so, *Becoming a Servant-Leader* offers a practical leadership philosophy that promotes the ethical use of power and creates an environment of trust, collaboration, and genuine communication. At its core, servant-leadership stems from a genuine commitment to service based on a carefully constructed and a deeply personal philosophy of leading by serving others. It is concerned with the moral obligation to society and the ability to make a positive contribution. It raises an important question for individuals and communities in leadership to address whether people experience growth, become healthier, wiser, freer and more autonomous.

If you intend to lead a group of people, you have to recognize their needs, you have to be a good listener, you have to participate in the important qualities of their work and recognize them on an individual basis. *Becoming a Servant-Leader* provides the tools for a leader to begin the journey of servant-leadership by balancing the needs of the group and individuals with the commitment to growth of people. This balancing act requires an inward journey with self and others that leads to an outward journey to committed service to the world.

While I am convinced that servant-leadership is the best form of leadership, each person must decide for him or herself. Such a decision does not come without a great deal of introspection and an honest appraisal of the motivation behind leadership: one who focuses on power or one who leads by serving others. My hope is that *Becoming a Servant-Leader* will give you the tools to make a difference in the world by becoming a servant-leader.

Rev. Dr. Quincy D. Brown

LaGrange College

Vice President for Spiritual Life and Church Relations

Fall 2012

why servant-leadership?

Katherine Elberfeld |

Founder, The Gabriel Center

for Servant-Leadership

At The Gabriel Center for Servant-Leadership, we are convinced that the time for servant-leadership is now. Voices throughout time have called us to lead as servants, to care more about those who have been entrusted to us than about our own needs, to learn how to listen, really listen, to what others have to say and to uphold the gifts, skills and dignity of every person. Servant-leaders do all that.

But most importantly, servant-leaders dig down deep to the causal roots of conflict and ferret them out so that they can be examined and understood. It is for this reason that the time for servant-leadership in the world is now. Now with an urgency never known before, we must understand that we can only resolve the conflicts in which we are involved and which threaten the well-being of humankind not through weapons but by identifying the core issues inherent in the contention and facilitating an understanding at that deepest level. Simply put, we must learn how to get along with each other or we, along with all the inhabitants of the Earth, and the planet itself are at risk.

And servant-leadership provides a powerful counterforce to that ultimate terror. As we all together live out our lives as servant-leaders, we live out a life of love — by sharing power and control; by deeply listening to each other; by finding ways to speak the truth in love; by committing to our relationships and shepherding them through crises and conflicts — we work together to push back at that ultimate terror and discover a proclamation of abundance: We come to know that when we love one another, we live in fullness, health, joy and peace.

When I first heard about The Gabriel Center, I had reserved thoughts. It sounded a bit too "churchy" for me. I knew that the concept for the Gabriel Center grew out of Katie Elberfeld's desire to combine her knowledge of experiential education, gained through Mid-Atlantic Training and Consulting, Inc., (MATC) and the concept of servant-leadership. I knew a lot about MATC — an organization that focused on intrapersonal and interpersonal awareness and skills as the basis for group dynamics, experiential education design skills, consultation skills and organization development. MATC was unique in its use of a disciplined reflection process that helped me learn a lot about myself and my interactions with others. After years of working on my own personal growth, I became a group trainer and trainer of trainers in that system. I asked myself: "Where is the MATC connection to servant-leadership?" And then, of course, I had to ask myself: "What does servant-leadership actually mean?"

I wondered if it implied an expectation that ordinary people should live up to bigger-than-life models like Jesus, Gandhi or the Buddha. Or was there something here that would speak to me and really build on the values I had gained from MATC? I began to read material from the Gabriel Center that included my introduction to Robert Greenleaf and his application of servant-leadership in everyday life in arenas ranging from interpersonal relationships to corporate philosophy.

I learned what servant-leadership is not. It is not another quick-fix management solution or the latest fad to hit the seminar circuit. Rather, it is a long-established, fundamental philosophy that generates remarkable results over time.

Servant-leadership stems from the clear understanding that all great leaders become great by first serving the needs of others. Research shows that those who master this concept and then put it into action consistently rise to the top of their fields. Why? Because only through an honest commitment to serving others can leaders draw upon their own creativity and talents and thereby help others achieve any kind of lasting change or meaningful success.

The concept began to make a lot of sense to me. I reflected on my own professional practice as a therapist and consultant and wondered what message I had been promoting. Whether my clients were individuals, ministers of foreign governments, United Nation representatives in developing countries, local leaders or church

| **Jacqueline Bahn-Henkelman, Ph.D**

International organization development consultant & coach

groups, the message has been: "In order to serve others effectively, it is necessary first to get to know yourself, including how you react and interact with those you represent or lead. Only then can you serve others in appropriate ways."

The concept of servant-leadership is not the norm in our society, and even when it is explicitly or implicitly accepted in a group or organization, issues like competition, mistrust or turfdom lie just below the surface to jeopardize our creativity and productivity. Yet with the ever-widening shadow of mistrust, hatred and war we experience across the world today, I can think of no better concept than servant-leadership. It really makes good sense that the experiential education concepts promoted by MATC can help individuals and groups put servant-leadership into practice.

In The Washington Post article, "A Dollop of Deeper American Values: Why 'Soft Power' Matters in Fighting Terrorism," Joseph S. Nye, Jr., laments how America's hard military power in Iraq removed a tyrant but cost the country much in terms of "soft power" to attract others. Nye, dean of Harvard's Kennedy School of Government, describes soft power as "the ability to get what we want by attracting others rather than by threatening or paying them. It is based on our culture, our political ideals and our policies." He refers to examples of how Americans have been good at using soft power, i.e., Franklin Delano Roosevelt's Four Freedoms in Europe after World War II, and how we broadcast American music and news behind the Iron Curtain. Nye asserts that "our leaders are going to have to learn to better combine soft and hard power into 'smart power.'"

Basically, that is what servant-leadership is: "smart power." It is not being too soft. It is what Roger Fisher and William Ury, authors of *Getting to Yes*, call being "soft on the person and hard on the problem."

Whether you and your organization use Becoming a Servant-Leader on your own or choose to work with a coach steeped in servant-leadership, you are taking a significant step toward serving others out of integrity, respect and that often scary to use word "love." There has never been a better time to put into practice the words from Burt Bacharach's song, "What the world needs now is love, sweet love ... ."

Leaders work in wondrous ways. Some assume great institutional burdens, others quietly deal with one (person) at a time.

Robert Greenleaf

The Servant as Leader

Within Robert Greenleaf's words lies one of the great conundrums of "good leadership" — is it possible to be a great leader within a huge bureaucracy? All institutions — education, healthcare, government and family systems — seek, sometimes desperately, for leadership, only to discover their search has been in vain. Why are there so many unhealthy leaders, a search committee member or patient seeking a diagnosis might ask. Why isn't Mom home in time for dinner more often? What is the pull to run a Fortune 500 company? And one might come back with a retort: Good leadership, excellent in fact, does exist in spiritual, commercial and ethical centers of civic and global activity. And what is good leadership? One might argue that it's simply education in its purest form. Education of the leader and of the follower must occur in harmonious tandem, even in the face of adversity and conflict, for true leadership to evolve in healthy, demonstrative and productive ways. Looking at the word educate at its very own root clarifies the role of education within institutions, be they miniscule or behemoth.

To educate. From the Latin, "to draw forth, to draw out." The two nouns spanning the hyphen in the binomial "servant-leader" work in tandem to draw forth the best learning possible. Robert Greenleaf's essay title "The Servant as Leader" gives away an almost dramatic role of the adverb "as" — the servant is posing as something, it is trying something on for size, and, we, the editors of this book, hope that you will try servant-leadership on for size. Chances are great that you already have, and if so, you too will benefit from the particular resources this guide has in store for you. The concepts are not new; in fact, they are rooted in the wisdom of the centuries: another way to summarize most briefly what you will encounter in these pages is by saying, "to thine own self be true; know thyself." For only in knowing ourselves fully are we able to teach others generously and boundlessly. With all that you bring to your experience with this book, and all that you can gain, you will be prepared to go out into the world and quietly deal with one person at a time, or you can take on an institution. And if you're lucky, you'll be able to do both — simultaneously.

| **Mark Elberfeld**

Communications Coordinator, The Gabriel Center for Servant-Leadership

servant-leadership: a better way

The term **servant-leader** entered the modern day mainstream with the publication of Robert K. Greenleaf's essay "The Servant as Leader," in 1970. Greenleaf served as director of management research and development at AT&T for many years before he became an author. During the 1960s, he worked as a consultant to some of America's top universities, foundations and businesses. During those years, Greenleaf observed and was troubled about student unrest on college campuses. He began noticing students reading books by Hermann Hesse and he, too, read many of Hesse's works. As a result, Greenleaf's concepts of a "servant-leader" were gleaned from Hesse's last book, *Journey to the East* (1956).

In the book, Hesse's character, Leo, is a servant to a group of people who are journeying to the East to join a spiritual religious order headed by a wise leader. Leo tends to menial chores, takes care of the animals and lifts spirits with his songs and stories. One day, Leo leaves and the group falls apart. Years later, the narrator of the story meets Leo in a large city and discovers that Leo was, in fact, the wise leader the group had sought. The one who was known as a servant had been their leader all along. Inspired by Hesse, Greenleaf provided this benchmark for servant-leaders in his 1970 essay:

> The best test is: Do those served grow as persons; do they, while being served, become healthier, wiser, freer, more autonomous, more likely themselves to become servants?

The phrase "servant-leader" is relatively new, but the idea is found in every ancient faith and wisdom tradition. In recent times, noted author Stephen Covey has written that servant-leadership is like a "force of nature, a template inscribed in the human psyche." However, the servant-leader concept is referenced in a wide range of works that span millennia. Here are just a few examples:

With the best of leaders,
When the work is done,
The project completed,
The people will say,
'We did it ourselves.'
Tao Te Ching 17
Lao Tse

One thing I know: the only ones among you who will really be happy are those who will have sought and found how to serve.
Dr. Albert Schweitzer

Servant-leadership has emerged as one of the dominant philosophies being discussed in the world today.
Indiana Business Journal

[A]nd Allah sees the servants. Those who say: Our Lord! surely we believe, therefore forgive us our faults and save us from the chastisement of the fire. The patient, and the truthful, and the obedient, and those who spend (benevolently) and those who ask forgiveness in the morning times.
The Family of Imran
Koran.003:3.15-17

So Jesus called them and said ... 'whoever would be first among you must be servant of all.'
Mark 10:44

There is something gracious and graceful about serving.
Maya Angelou, U.S. poet and author

Make no mistake about it, as a Starfleet officer you will never have a more satisfying assignment than when serving among others with whom you share mutual dependence ... an interconnection ... even a symbiotic relationship ... It is prudent that you be driven to serve purposes outside your own self-interest, as the extreme individualist never succeeds as an officer ... Make it so.

Excerpts from Captain Jean Luc Picard's personal journal,

Make It So: Leadership Lessons From Star Trek: The Next Generation

Bill Ross and Wess Robertson

Indeed, we debated for a long time on the research team about how to describe the good-to-great leaders. Initially, we penciled in terms like 'selfless executive' and 'servant leader.'

Good to Great: Why Some Companies Make the Leap ... And Others Don't

Jim Collins

Defining Servant & Leader

The words "servant" and "leader" can elicit mental and emotional responses. Take a few minutes individually to write down the thoughts that come to mind for those words. If you are in a group, have each person share his or her associations with these words.

Servant————————————————————————————— **Leader**

The paradox of servant-leadership: The hyphen between the two words reminds us of the tension and the balance to be found in serving others and leading.

After years of reviewing Greenleaf's writings, Larry C. Spears, former chief executive officer of The Greenleaf Center for Servant-Leadership, identified ten characteristics central to the development of servant-leaders:

listening: Servant-leaders not only practice active listening by being attentive to others, they listen on the inside by being conscientious to their inner voices and spirit.

empathy: The servant-leader attempts to enter into the feeling and spirit of the other person and conveys that quality with genuine feeling and words, reflecting what the other is saying.

healing: Servant-leaders have the opportunity to "help make whole" others with whom they come in contact — a process that not only transforms the individuals but the servant-leaders as well.

awareness: Servant-leaders make a strong commitment to self-awareness — the ongoing effort to examine themselves and the impact of their actions on others.

persuasion: The servant-leader seeks to be effective at building consensus rather than trying to coerce compliance.

conceptualization: Servant-leaders have the ability to raise their sights from the day-to-day-challenges and create a broader vision.

foresight: An intuitive characteristic, foresight enables the servant-leader to understand the lessons from the past, the realities of the present and the ramifications of future decisions.

stewardship: Servant-leadership assumes first and foremost a commitment to serving the needs of others.

commitment to the growth of people: The servant-leader recognizes the tremendous responsibility to do everything within his or her power to nurture the personal, professional and spiritual growth of each individual within the organization or community.

building community: A servant-leader understands that building relationships is at the core of shaping and nurturing human lives.

The Gabriel Center has built on the work of Greenleaf and others to identify specific characteristics that define a servant-leader and describe what makes a servant-leader unique — different from other leadership models and traditions. They include:

choice: One chooses to serve first; also chooses to lead, to "go out ahead and show the way."

humility: Respects differences, embraces diversity, understands potential for mistakes.

mutual accountability: Fosters a sense in the group that each member is responsible to him- or herself and to the whole; values working relationships as well as financial results. Embraces mutual reviews.

agent of change: Understands that deep transformation happens in community with others.

deep reflection: Accesses intuition and foresight to strengthen one's leadership abilities and inform decisions; goes beyond theory to look at applications in real life.

Characterizing Servant-Leaders

What are other characteristics that set servant-leaders apart?

additional characteristics:

As we explore servant-leadership, we find that it is like a prism with many facets — it's hard to confine it to a narrow definition, but we can begin to understand the concept by looking at some of its basic tenets, at some of the facets of the prism. Here are some of them:

- Developing our own sense and style of servant-leadership is a lifelong process — not a quick fix.
- It starts with personal awareness — the better we know ourselves, the better able we are to lead others.
- It has to do with behaviors rather than what particular setting we're in, job we're doing or task we're working on.
- We learn to be comfortable with paradox as we develop our servant-leadership style.
- Sharing power and control is inherent to servant-leadership; engaging in collaborative decision-making processes rather than the top-down model so prevalent in many sectors of society.
- We learn from reflection on experience rather than experience alone.
- And, very importantly, we are all leaders.

Most of us have people in our life, either in the past or currently, who exemplify the tenets of servant-leadership. These are people who hold us in trust, who listen without imposing their will or agenda and who are committed to our growth and development.

Write the names of those you know in your life whom you admire as examples of people who lead by serving. It could be a family member, a teacher, a coach or a friend. What, specifically, did they do to serve you? What lessons have you learned from them?

 Servant-Leaders in Your Life

_____

name   **lessons**

A BETTER WAY TO LEAD | Servant-leadership is a simple philosophy: Those who lead serve, and those who serve lead by example. Just as a goose flying in formation provides extra lift to the birds it leads, servant-leaders foster an environment for their colleagues and family members that brings their strengths forward in the most positive way.

Concern for People

vs. Concern for Task

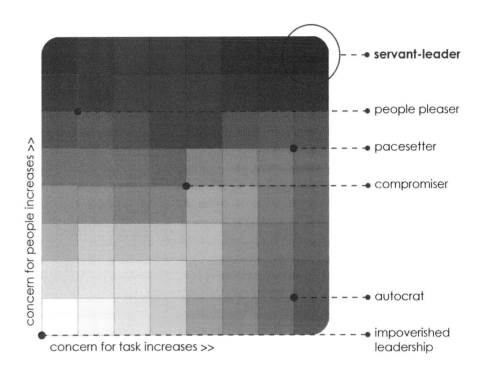

servant-leader: the most effective leaders recognize the importance of people in achieving success.

people pleaser: desire to please outweighs the need to succeed.

pacesetter: focus on task overshadows need for healthy work environment.

compromiser: consensus-only decisions means the tough choices are not made.

autocrat: top-down authority precludes valuable input.

impoverished leadership: in the absence of passion and motivation, nothing can be achieved.

Many forms of leadership pit a concern for task against a concern for people. Servant-leadership, however, holds a high concern for task and a high concern for people in balance. This combination results in creating the healthiest environment for success in your personal and your professional life. We believe this is a better way.

equipment for the servant-leader journey

In the movie *Rain Man* (1988), the character played by Tom Cruise takes his autistic brother, played by Dustin Hoffman, on a road trip in their father's old car. They drive west, the direction that has always symbolized the possibility of new life in the American myth. Their journey is not only about the geographic destination; it is also about the inner journey of Cruise's character toward maturity, and the movement of Hoffman's character outward, toward the real world.

The servant-leader journey — for you personally as well as the people with whom you work in your organizations and communities — has the same two components:

> • The **inward journey** as a true seeker who develops his or her gifts, faces fears and challenges, listens, and serves; and

> • The **outward journey** as a change agent transforming organizational structures and contributing to the health of the world and its people.

A common trait among servant-leaders is that they are continual seekers and active listeners. They use all kinds of experiences to increase their awareness about themselves and deepen their understanding of others.

Becoming a Servant-Leader is designed so that individuals and groups can direct themselves in their servant-leader exploration and develop the skills necessary for the journey. This section provides the framework necessary for using this workbook and the concepts outlined here will reappear in the activities throughout the rest of the workbook.

The servant-leader journey has four main stages, and they each build on the other.   The lines between the stages are fluid and moveable, but the developmental process clearly begins with an awareness of one's self, as illustrated below.

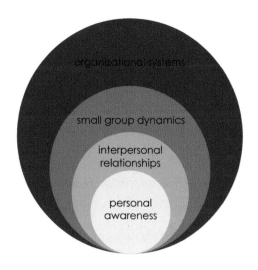

As Stephen Covey writes in The 7 Habits of Highly Effective People:

> Change — real change — comes from the inside out. It doesn't come from hacking at the leaves of attitude and behavior with quick fix personality ethic techniques. It comes from striking at the root — the fabric of our thought, the fundamental, essential paradigms, which give definition to our character and create the lens with which we see the world.

Building on the foundation of healthy personal awareness, we move to interactions with one other person, the interpersonal relationships that we encounter; interactions within groups; and functioning within the organizational systems in which we are involved. But ultimately, the journey begins by learning about ourselves.

In *Becoming a Servant-Leader*, learning opportunities are all based upon **experiential learning**. Each adult has already developed a learning style with which he or she is most comfortable; however, decades of research have shown that adults learn the most through actual experience. Doing the real thing surpasses every other activity for adult learning, as shown in the Adult Cone of Experience.

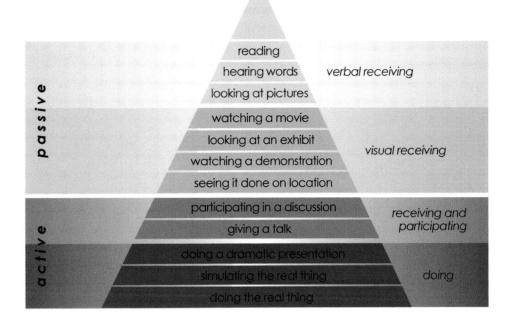

Kurt Lewin, the founder of social psychology, applied the scientific method to social interactions in suggesting the following stages in experiential learning: concrete experience, observations and reflections, formulations of abstract concepts and generalizations, and testing implications of concepts in new situations. Data are gathered from as many sources as possible to bring new understanding and the opportunity for change of behavior.

To use experience for real learning, you need to understand a cycle that requires **disciplined reflection** on your experience. This core practice of servant-leaders is the key to total understanding of the learning process. Servant-leaders discipline themselves to follow a process that allows them to hear and honor the perceptions of others. In this way, they open themselves to change, begin to trust others more and deepen their personal interactions with others.

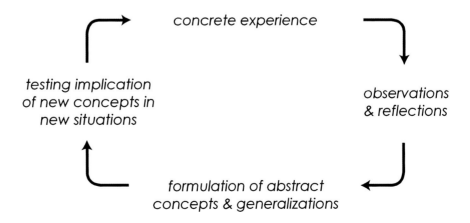

Kurt Lewin's Stages of Experiential Learning

One effective way to engage in disciplined reflection is to follow a sequential process called the **E-I-A-G Experiential Learning Cycle**. This cycle can be applied to individuals, groups and organizations in order to learn from experience. Exercises in applying E-I-A-G cycles will appear throughout this workbook.

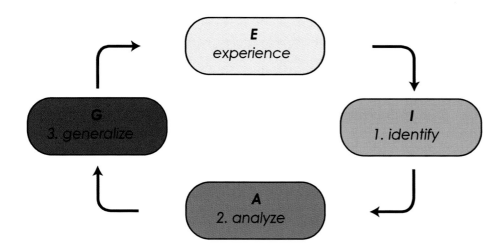

EIAG Experiential Learning Cycle

Refer to the E-I-A-G cycle illustration, and note the numbers 1, 2, and 3, which appear with "**I**dentify," "**A**nalyze," and "**G**eneralize," respectively. These steps follow an experience, and are known as **I-A-G** (pronounced "EYE-ag"). Let's examine them more closely:

1. Identify (Looking at what has happened)
Select a specific event from which you (or others) wish to learn. It can be either a positive, uncomfortable or problematic event.

2. Analyze (Thinking about what has happened)
The specific event that has been identified must be described by those who experienced it. The person or persons whose behavior is being examined must first give permission for the analysis. Then those present describe the chosen event from their perspectives, and the person whose behavior is being examined responds last. The description will include what each person saw, thought, felt and did when the event occurred, and the assumptions that were generated. The purpose is to understand more clearly the cause-and-effect relationships.

3. Generalize (Planning for another time)
Generalizing means drawing conclusions from the reflections and

adapted from "Experiential Learning: How to Learn From Experience" by Nancy Geyer and A. Lee Schomer

anticipating actions that might be chosen when a similar event occurs in the future. On the basis of the analysis, participants can plan for the future and make decisions about what changes — in behaviors, approach or climate — would be helpful in a similar situation for the individual, the group or the organization.

Greenleaf wrote that a servant-leader should operate with high awareness. Your ability to remain open and aware is a valuable step on the servant-leader journey. The Gabriel Center has adopted the E-I-A-G Experiential Learning Cycle as a practical way to fulfill the expectation that servant-leaders are reflective leaders who will learn from their experiences.

Robert K. Greenleaf: a brief biography

by Don M. Frick

Great leaders are seen as servants first, and that simple fact is the key to their greatness.

Robert K. Greenleaf

"The Servant as Leader"

The person who brought the philosophy of servant-leadership into the 20th century lived his ideas before he wrote them. Born in Terre Haute, Indiana, in 1904, Robert K. Greenleaf died in 1990.

Throughout most of his life, he was an introvert. Yet, Bob Greenleaf aspired to make a difference in the world. He was able to focus his ambition when, during his last year at Carleton College in 1926, a professor made this comment: "Large institutions are taking over many of the functions of caring in our society. If you really want to make a difference, get hired by a big organization and try to change it from within." When he graduated, he took a job with AT&T, then the world's largest organization.

Because he was a college graduate, Greenleaf soon was tapped to train AT&T field managers, who were gaining promotion. These grizzled veterans knew far more about the job to be done than the young "whippersnapper" Greenleaf. However, Bob was smart enough to listen and learn from his "students." He developed a way of facilitating reflection and helping others learn from their own experience. Decades later, his approach to adult learning would be formally discovered and solidified by Kurt Lewin and the National Training Labs.

Meanwhile, at AT&T, Bob quickly rose to director of management development. He consistently turned down other promotions, because he believed his position allowed him to better influence AT&T's values and human development. As he traveled around the country, he noticed the biggest problem of AT&T's underperforming units was a lack of able leadership. Yet, he came to believe that the most powerful kind of leadership had nothing to do with one's position, but depended upon a person's ability to build, support and serve others; to act with integrity, listen deeply, articulate a vision and still demand accountability. He began to develop ways of training leaders and managers for a kind of leadership that went far beyond the "Great Man" or "John Wayne" leadership models prevalent at that time.

At AT&T, Robert Greenleaf instituted the first systematic programs of managerial and leadership evaluation. He pioneered some of today's familiar techniques, such as "360 evaluations." He invited theologians and psychologists and statesmen to spend time with AT&T managers. Yet, he consistently had to show that his work contributed to AT&T's financial bottom line. Consequently, the AT&T presidents with whom he worked closely perceived that these innovative approaches to teaching and learning were important for positive business results.

In 1964, at the age of 60, Robert Greenleaf took an early retirement from AT&T so he could broaden his scope of influence. He co-founded an organization, The Center for Applied Ethics, to consult with a variety of organizations about ethical decisions. Bob worked with foundations and university presidents across America during the tumultuous 1960s and '70s. It was after a spectacular failure in a consultancy that Bob Greenleaf came up with the phrase servant-leader. He was looking for language to express the idea that people and organizations should care first about those they lead. He remembered the character of Leo in a book he had read by Hermann Hesse. That book, Journey to the East, described how a group of seekers of wisdom traveled to the East (the direction of enlightenment) to join a religious order. During their journey, a man named Leo served as their cook, porter and general organizer. He also kept motivation high with songs and jokes. One day, Leo left unexpectedly, and the group fell into disarray without his help. Years later, the narrator of the story met Leo and discovered that all along, Leo had been the head of the religious order the group had sought so many years ago. Leo, the leader, had presented himself as a servant. The servant was the leader precisely because he had served first. When he remembered this story, Greenleaf put together the two words: servant and leader.

In 1970, Robert Greenleaf published an essay called "The Servant as Leader," which humanized his thinking about the essence of individual leadership. Two years later he wrote a companion piece, "The Institution as Servant," in which he argued that whole organizations could function as servants. In 1974, he finished his famous trilogy with an essay called "Trustees as Servants," which explored the unique role of trustees in organizations. All three essays, plus additional writings, were collected in a book titled *Servant Leadership* (Paulist Press, 1976). A publishing phenomenon, this book has influenced current motivational authors such as Peter Senge, Stephen Covey, Ken Blanchard and Margaret Wheatley. Greenleaf's publications have sold over 500,000 copies worldwide. Today, the Greenleaf Center for Servant-Leadership in Indianapolis has eight international affiliates.

Robert K. Greenleaf wrote his own epitaph. Throughout his life, he enjoyed working with his hands in his basement workshop and continued to identify with the common working folks of his Hoosier state. It was no surprise to those who knew him that his epitaph read: "Potentially a good plumber. Ruined by a sophisticated education."

The longer we live, the more our experience widens; the less prone are we to judge our neighbour's conduct, to question the world's wisdom: wherever an accumulation of small defences is found ... there, be sure, it is needed. I always, through my whole life, liked to penetrate to the real truth ... To see and know the worst is to take from Fear her main advantage.

Charlotte Brontë

Villette

Becoming a Servant-Leader begins with personal awareness. In this section, we start the inward journey by developing the skills needed to have a deeper understanding of our inner selves. The Johari Window model will serve as a guide to your understanding relationships in terms of awareness, feedback and learning through reflection on experience. Reflective questions will help you map your servant-leader journey. These tools, along with the personal awareness EIAG, emotional intelligence and harnessing intuition, will prepare you for learning how to communicate with others.

through the Johari Window

For the servant-leader it is essential to understand one's self to be able to understand and work with others. The **Johari Window**, created by behavioral scientists Joseph Luft and Harry Ingham, has been used for decades to help people understand relationships in terms of such awareness. The model helps you become more aware of your own behaviors that are unknown to you but are known by others. The Johari Window also enables you to understand how sharing parts of your hidden self opens up and facilitates communication.

known to self	*not known to self*	
I	II	
Open	**Blind**	*known to others*
III	IV	
Hidden	**Unknown**	*not known to others*

The Johari Window

quadrant I: The open area refers to behavior and motivation known to self and known to others.

quadrant II: The blind area is the area in which others can see aspects of you that are unknown to you.

quadrant III: The hidden area represents that which you know about yourself but do not reveal to others, such as a hidden agenda or matters about which you have sensitive feelings.

quadrant IV: The unknown area represents behaviors, feelings and motivations that are unknown to self and others. Some may become known in the future, and, at that time, you may realize that these unknown behaviors, feelings or motives have been influencing your behavior all along.

As you work with the Johari model, the following are principles to remember:

- A change in any one quadrant will affect all other quadrants.
- It takes energy to hide, deny or to be blind to behavior that is involved in interaction.
- Forced awareness is undesirable and usually ineffective.
- Threat tends to decrease awareness while mutual trust tends to increase awareness.
- Interpersonal learning means a change has taken place so that the "open" area is larger, and one or more of the other areas has grown smaller.
- Working with others is facilitated by a large "open" area. It means more of the resources and skills in the membership can be applied to the task at hand.
- The smaller the first quadrant, the poorer the communication.
- There is universal curiosity about the unknown area, but this is held in check by custom, social training, trust and safety issues and diverse fears.
- Sensitivity means appreciating the covert aspects of behavior in Quadrants II, III, and IV and respecting the desires of others to keep them so.

Individuals can use the E-I-A-G to expand their "open" area in their Johari Window by receiving feedback from others about how they are perceived. This is especially useful in a group of people who have no prior knowledge of each other. Feedback offered to an individual by other people during an I-A-G (Identify-Analyze-Generalize) reflection process reduces the person's "blind" area in the Johari Window.

step 1: Begin by having an individual stand or sit in front of the group and ask the other members to recall what their first impressions were of this person when the group convened. (That person will now be referred to as Samuel.) The facilitator then asks: *What were your first impressions of Samuel when this group convened?* The recollection is the "identification" part of the I-A-G experience to be analyzed. (If no one in the group volunteers, the facilitator may lead the process using himself or herself.)

step 2: Samuel remains silent while the facilitator elicits the thoughts, feelings, and actions of group members by asking the questions: *What did you think when you first encountered Samuel? What were your feelings? What did you do?* Most of the responses to these questions are data that would have been in Samuel's "blind" area of the Johari Window and is the first part of the analysis in the I-A-G reflection process.

step 3: The facilitator can then continue the analysis by checking assumptions that members of the group have about Samuel. The facilitator will next ask Samuel how these responses fit with his own self-perception.

step 4: To assist Samuel in learning more about himself from the first impressions of others, the facilitator asks the following: *What insights did you gain? What does this mean for you in the future?* This is the "generalize" step of the I-A-G reflection process.

The first pane of the Johari Window is now open a bit more for all involved.

Now let's look at an example of how Johari and personal E-I-A-G can work together to improve self-awareness.

 Johari Window
Sample Script

Samuel and Teresa were co-leaders for the annual meeting of a servant-leader association. They had been given the responsibility to plan this annual meeting for the fifty members who had come from many different parts of the country. Teresa was a well known leader, but Samuel was relatively new to the group. At the beginning of the meeting Samuel decided to model good servant-leader behavior by using the *I-A-G* reflection process. He thought that by doing this he would become more self-aware and enhance his ability to lead. After a brief opening, he asked Teresa to facilitate the *I-A-G* reflection process. Following is a script of this part of the meeting:

Teresa: Samuel has asked me to facilitate a reflection process for him so he can become more aware of how he is perceived. He wants to know what your first impressions were of him. Are you ready, Samuel, to receive this feedback?

Samuel: Sure, I'm ready.

Teresa: [to Samuel] I'm going to ask others their first impressions of you. I'd like you to just listen at first; you'll get a chance to talk after you have heard a sample of the first impressions.

Samuel: OK.

Teresa: [to the group] You've had a brief experience of Samuel here in the past few minutes as we've opened this meeting. As you think about that experience, what are your first impressions of Samuel? What did you think when you first saw Samuel today?

Sariel: When I first saw Samuel, I thought he looked like an intelligent young man who should be able to lead us in this annual meeting.

Ted: Yeah, I thought I would really like to get to know Samuel.

He's wearing a tweed jacket just like mine; he must have good taste.

Teresa: [to the group] Were there other thoughts that you had when you first saw Samuel?

Myriam: My reaction was different from Ted's. I thought that Samuel looked a little bit too much like a professor.

Teresa: [to Myriam] It sounds as though you have some feelings behind that statement. Will you share those feelings?

Myriam: I felt a little cautious; maybe a little uncomfortable. Actually I'm feeling a little uncomfortable sharing this.

Teresa: [to Myriam] I appreciate your sharing your feelings. Samuel really does want to know how others perceive him. [to the group] Were there others who shared Myriam's thoughts or feelings?

Alex: I picked up on that same impression of Samuel. I thought that I might get a lecture from him. But I always try to be careful not to jump to conclusions, so I didn't hold that thought too long. However, I was a little wary.

Teresa: [to the group] Were there other impressions?

Fred: When I came in the room and first saw Samuel, I thought he looked like a friendly person.

Teresa: [to Fred] Any feelings associated with that thought?

Fred: Sure, I was quite comfortable that he would be a co-leader of this meeting.

Teresa: [to Fred] Did you act on your thought and feeling?
Fred: Yep, I walked over to Samuel and introduced myself and

suggested that we find an opportunity to talk later.

Teresa: [to the group] Were there any different first impressions of Samuel? [hearing no further comments] For those of you who have responded, what assumptions were you making about Samuel?

Myriam: I suppose I made the assumption that anyone who wears a tweed jacket must be a college professor. I've never been comfortable around college professors.

Teresa: [to the group] Any other assumptions?

Fred: I probably made an assumption that since he smiled at me when I first saw him, it would be fun to have a conversation with him.

Teresa: [to the group] Any more assumptions? [hearing no further comments, to Samuel] Now that you've heard some of the first impressions, will you tell us what you thought you would hear?

Samuel: I always figure that I am a friendly guy. So Fred reacted to me just the way I find most satisfying. And although I don't like to hear that I look too professorial, I actually am a college professor.

Teresa: [to Samuel] What did you learn from this reflection of others' first impressions of you?

Samuel: I am more aware that not everyone experiences me as the nice friendly guy that I think I am. It is hard for me to realize that someone might be uncomfortable or cautious approaching me. I expect that Myriam and I might have a very fruitful conversation about college professors. Actually I want to learn a little more about what it is that creates that impression so quickly. Is it my tweed jacket?

Teresa: [to Samuel] I, too, can imagine you and Myriam having a most interesting conversation. And I know you will make time to talk with Fred. Are there any other ways in which you think you will be doing anything differently as a result of what you have learned in the last few minutes?

Samuel: [to Teresa] While I am co-leading this meeting, I intend to be aware of when I might be moving into a lecture format. I really don't want to make Myriam or anyone else uncomfortable. After all I am not here to give a lecture.

Samuel: [to the group] I really do appreciate the opportunity to enhance my awareness of how I am perceived.

Teresa: [to the group] This seems to be the time to turn to the first item on the agenda.

Samuel: [to Teresa and the group] Thanks, Teresa; I'm ready. Lead on.

The following page contains a summary sheet for using the E-I-A-G with the Johari Window, helping you to learn more about yourself from others.

E Experience

An individual's experience with members of a group.

I Identify

To individual:

About which aspects of yourself do you want to know others' reactions?

A Analyze

To others:

What do you think about the identified aspect of the individual?
How do you feel about it?
What have you done about it?
What assumptions are you making?

To individual:

What are the assumptions that you have about this aspect of yourself?
Do your assumptions match others' assumptions?

G Generalize

To individual:

What did you learn from your reflection?

What insights did you gain?

What applications do you see for the future?

emotional intelligence

The concept of **Emotional Intelligence (Ei)** was originally conceived by psychologists Peter Salovey and John Mayer. In *Working with Emotional Intelligence*, Daniel Goleman describes Ei as "the capacity for recognizing our own feelings and those of others, for motivating ourselves, and for managing emotions well in our relationships." Margaret Chapman in her *Emotional Intelligence Pocketbook* describes Ei as the learned ability to perceive, understand and express feelings accurately and control feelings so they work for us, not against us.

Numerous theorists claim Ei is the most important component of effective leadership. Ei includes both intrapersonal and interpersonal awareness. Intrapersonal skills are needed for self-management, whereas Interpersonal skills are needed to manage relationships with others.

personal awareness: (intrapersonal) The ability to see yourself with your own eyes, to be aware of your emotions and their effect on others; understanding your own goals, beliefs, values, drivers, rules – shoulds, musts and oughts – and the inner voice that gives you a sense of self-worth and your own capabilities.

emotional management: (intrapersonal) Keeping disruptive emotions and impulses under control; trying to understand the link between your interpretation of an event and your responses to it before acting; displaying honesty, integrity and trustworthiness.

self-motivation: (intrapersonal) Managing your internal state, harnessing your emotions and channeling them in the appropriate direction to result in higher levels of motivation and success.

relationship management: (interpersonal) A healthy relationship occurs when two or more people come together for mutual benefit. Managing a relationship is more than being nice or sociable. It requires being able to read the emotional climate, actively listening, showing empathy, including others' opinions and building bonds that create the desire in others to join together, lead or be led for mutual purposes.

Below are some questions organized into categories that can help you assess and improve your Ei. Think of a person whose relationship you value as you respond to the questions.

Assessing Personal Ei

Reciprocity
How supportive do you think you are of the person whose relationship you value?

How supportive is that person of you?

Is there mutual exchange?

Is the give and take in the relationship balanced?

In what way might the exchange be one-sided?

Skills
Would the other person consider you an active listener?

Do you practice empathy?

Endurance

Will the relationship grow as time continues? Why?

Is there mutual trust in the relationship? Upon what foundation is the trust built?

Tips toward **strengthening effective relationships**:

• Know the boundaries. What can and cannot be said or done?

• Check out expectations. Respect each other's needs and wants.

• Review your perceptions. Avoid making assumptions.

• Explore the other person's perception of you. Take a risk; ask yourself, "What is the worst that can happen?"

• Examine interactions. Consider what has worked well and what has not worked as well, and why this might be the case.

• Determine the desired outcomes. Set goals that have the power to improve your relationships.

A servant-leader teaches or leads by example. It is important to develop emotional capabilities, strive to resolve differences or solve problems in an inclusive manner, to communicate effectively and to demonstrate motivation.

Goleman explains in his 1998 *Harvard Business Review* article, "What Makes a Leader?" that people are born with a certain amount of Ei and that it generally improves with maturity. However, it also can be learned through deliberate reflection and feedback. Ei is governed primarily by the neurotransmitters of the brain's limbic system, which governs feelings, impulses and drives. The limbic system functions best when one is motivated to learn and through extended practice and feedback.

Experiential learning is an excellent way both to test your Ei and, through feedback, to improve it. A disciplined reflection process used after a meeting shows how individuals can learn from reflecting on that experience.

People with a high IQ can struggle in their working relationships with others, while those with a modest IQ can do surprisingly well. IQ plus Ei equals success — and Ei can be improved.

For more than 50 years, organizations have valued Ei enough to send their top executives to training to learn more about and begin to improve their intrapersonal and interpersonal skills. The National Training Laboratories and the American Management Association for many years have been two well-known organizations providing training that enhances Ei.

However, improving Ei is not a one-time effort. For example, coaching — in life skills, management and leadership — has become a highly successful way for individuals to work toward improving intrapersonal and interpersonal skills in their work and other settings. Generally, a coaching relationship is spread out over a specified period of time that allows the person being coached opportunities to identify areas for improvement, experiment with new behavior, reflect on the effects of the behavior and receive feedback. Remember, behavioral change takes time.

Joining a group of people with similar interests in which everyone is committed to setting goals and receiving feedback is also an excellent way to work toward improving personal relationships and Ei. The most important ingredient is being open to learning about yourself and how you affect and are affected by others.

harnessing intuition and foresight

Intuition is that inner feeling, a "sixth sense," that says "go this way."

Foresight is an intuitive characteristic, enabling the servant-leader to understand the lessons from the past, the realities of the present and the ramifications of future decisions.

Those who are serious about accessing intuition and foresight increase the odds of learning in this way by setting aside special times for reflection. Computer pioneer Seymour Cray, who designed the first, fastest and most powerful supercomputers in the world, had his best insights late at night, away from the distractions of his office. The theory of relativity occurred to Albert Einstein during a time of relaxation. He was lying on the sun-dappled grass watching the sky. For fun, he began to imagine what it would be like to ride on a sunbeam. From that idle speculation, he developed understandings that forever changed our picture of the universe. All his life, Einstein continued to harness imagination for serious purposes by conducting "thought experiments," especially when the equipment to test his theories did not yet exist.

You also need to deal with "information gaps" associated with making important decisions. Part of a leader's duty is to gather numbers, facts and research before choosing which action to take, but you can only go so far with such data. You can never know everything — or even enough. The more complex the decision, the wider the information gap between what you know and what you need to know.

what we already |||||||||||||||||||| information gap |||||||||||||||||||| what we need to know   know

The following are **tips for accessing your intuition and foresight** and questions to help you discover your own style in this process of self discovery:

cultivate personal awareness: How can you use the Johari model in your daily life? With your family? Your work colleagues? In the community?

do your homework and ask fresh questions: What new questions can you ask when faced with a new opportunities or difficult challenges?

let go of certainty: What is the scariest certainty you could give up? What is the worst that could happen if you did that?

make time and space for reflection: Where and when can you find time for reflection? Do you have a strategy to relax, clear your mind and discern the wisdom of intuition?

use the power of sleep: Try keeping a pencil and pad by your bed and document even the most outrageous dreams. Also write down fleeting thoughts and images that occur during the states just before sleeping and after waking.

dream the big dream: Can you embrace a dream as rich and inspiring as your tremendous powers of mind and spirit? What keeps you from dreaming big? Write down your big dream anyway!

live life on two levels: What do you do to harness the power of reflection? What you do is to let the idea go — basically, you don't do anything at all. Here are a few guidelines: Access both your right brain and your left brain as you gather factual data and tap into the inner perspective of intuition and foresight. Living on two levels combines the practical rationality of western thought with the contemplation of eastern tradition.

intuition can communicate itself in various ways: Pay attention to shifting emotions, changes in muscle tension and those fleeting images, sounds, words or feelings that appear to make no sense. You may find that they contain crazy wisdom that you can use in new and refreshing ways.

The servant-leader makes time and space for reflection. As you examine your servant-leader gifts and skills, use the E-I-A-G reflection process in order to expedite growth in your journey. This work usually involves a quiet time in which you are intentional about the reflection. The activity as outlined is designed for individual reflecting through journal writing.

1: Think of a recent experience that had an emotional impact on you when you either were in a leadership position or could have asserted leadership and didn't. Record this as the experience part of the E-I-A-G in your journal.

2: Identify a specific critical incident in that experience upon which you want to focus. Describe in your journal the setting or scene and what happened that initiated the critical incident. Record this as the identification in your journal.

3: For the first part of the analysis, remember your thoughts at the time of the critical incident. What were your feelings? What were your assumptions? What did you do? Record this in your journal as part of the analysis.

4: For the second part of the analysis, note how others reacted. You may not know the internal thoughts, feelings, actions, and assumptions of others unless they were shared. What you do know or imagine can be recorded in your journal as part of the analysis.

5: Compare your reactions with the characteristics of the sevant-leader. Are they in harmony? In what way are they different? Record this as part of the analysis.

6: What insights do you have about your servant-leader journey? What will you do the same or differently in the future? Record these as your generalization from the reflection.

This reflection process can be applied to any aspect of your life's journey. Use the E-I-A-G to reflect after a critical incident occurs that has some emotional impact on you. This internal E-I-A-G can also be used in a group in which each individual has his or her own experience and then shares the reflection or the learnings with the group. Here is an example:

Samuel: [reflecting in a journal] During the second day of the servant-leader association's annual meeting, I was facilitating in the morning with about 50 persons present. Everything was going along fine until it seemed as though the agenda were hijacked from me. We had been discussing a disappointing treasurer's report describing the association's indebtedness when an incident occurred that changed the agenda to the subject of how we don't support our officers when they are people of color. We worked on this new agenda with one of the members of the group who stepped forward to facilitate while I stepped aside.

The incident that I want to reflect upon is how I, and others, reacted to a brief interchange between two members while the disappointing treasurer's report was being presented:

Fred: [white male] These figures are appalling. How did we get in such a financial mess? If we'd had stronger leadership, this wouldn't have happened.

Yvonne: [black female] That sounds like an attack on our president, Mary. I believe that if the president were a white male instead of a black female, we would have supported her, and we wouldn't have such a negative financial report.

Samuel: *What were my reactions?* I remember feeling tense. I was uncertain about what to do. We had other agenda items including an important presentation about how to deal with the financial situation. I was torn internally between a desire to direct the meeting back to the agenda we had set and the demands of the interchange that was on the floor. Here I was as a white male facilitating an issue that was potentially divisive

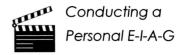 *Conducting a Personal E-I-A-G*

| *Experience*

| *Identification*

| *Analysis*

regardless of the actions I took. I was hesitant.

What were others' reactions? Louise immediately stood up and came to the front of the group. Louise was a white female who had extensive experience and an impeccable reputation as a diversity facilitator.

Louise: [to the group and me] I think we should deal with the issue in front of us right now. We always sweep it under the rug. I have an exercise that I can lead that will help us gain greater understanding in addressing this issue.

Me: [to Louise] Go right ahead.

Teresa: (my co-leader) [to Louise]: That's fine with me. It seemed that Teresa and I had totally capitulated. I want to think about what a servant-leader, who was fully present in the moment, might have done other than the 'knee jerk reaction' of letting Louise facilitate the meeting.

Samuel: *What would a servant-leader do?* It is true that a servant-leader desires to serve first. It is also true that the servant-leader makes the choices and leads while always carefully assessing the impact on people. I was displaying many of the characteristics of a servant-leader. However, in this case I believe that I accommodated too quickly to Louise rather than asserting my leadership role.

Generalization |

Samuel: My learning is clear in this case. My tendency to accommodate to others sometimes prevents me from being fully present to the moment and to my responsibility as co-leader.

In a future similar situation, I would try a different approach. Since I was hesitant and unsure what to do, I would suggest that my co-leader, Teresa, and I dialogue briefly in front of the group about different alternatives and the consequences of these actions. I might invite Louise and Yvonne to join the conversation about how to proceed before continuing with the planned agenda or revising it.

You can refer to the following summary sheet when using the E-I-A-G as the framework for your personal journal:

 Experience
A different experience for each person.

 Identify
What happened for you that was especially significant?
Was there a critical incident that had an emotional impact?

Analyze
What were your thoughts, feelings and actions?
What assumptions did you have?
What were others' thoughts, feelings and actions?
What was your intent?
Did what happened match your intent?
(Some of these data are not known to you unless you checked with others involved.)

Generalize
What insights do you have?
What learnings do you have about yourself?
What applications do you see for the future?

Do not recklessly spill the waters of your mind in this direction and in that, lest you become like a spring lost and dissipated in the desert. But draw them together into a little compass, and hold them still, so still; And let them become clear, so clear — so limpid, so mirror-like; At last the mountains and the sky shall glass themselves in peaceful beauty ... and Love himself shall come and bend over and catch his own likeness in you.

Edward Carpenter, "The Lake of Beauty"

A New Zealand Prayer Book

We are not always in a state of strong emotion, and when we are calm we can use our memories and gradually change the bias of our fear, as we do our tastes.

George Eliot, *Daniel Deronda*

To know how to choose a path with heart is to learn how to follow intuitive feeling. Logic can tell you superficially where a path might lead to, but it cannot judge whether your heart will be in it.

Jean Shinoda Bolen, M.D., psychiatrist and author

If you don't understand yourself, you don't understand anybody else.

Nikki Giovanni

U.S. poet

Great leaders move us. They ignite our passion and inspire the best in us. When we try to explain why they are so effective, we speak of strategy, vision, or powerful ideas. But the reality is much more primal: Great leadership works through the emotions.

Daniel Goleman et al.

Primal Leadership

I believe the power of observation in numbers of very young children to be quite wonderful for its closeness and accuracy. Indeed, I think that most grown men (and women) who are remarkable in this respect, may with greater propriety be said not to have lost the faculty, than to have acquired it; and rather, as I generally observe such men (and women) to retain a certain freshness, and gentleness, and capacity of being pleased, which are also an inheritance they have preserved from their childhood.

Charles Dickens

David Copperfield

All human interactions are opportunities either to learn or to teach.

M. Scott Peck

Equipped with a fuller understanding of our inner selves, we now begin the outward part of our journey, first by considering how we relate to one other person. In this section, we will develop communication skills so important to the servant-leader, with particular focus on learning to listen actively and to give and receive feedback in a productive manner. As you will see, such skills not only contribute to interpersonal growth, but your own personal awareness will continue to deepen as you apply these essential disciplines.

the art of listening

For many, listening is simply hearing what someone says, deciphering the sounds into words and ideas, and waiting for their turn to speak. For a servant-leader, listening involves more than simply being in the same physical space with someone else or thinking about what to say next. The ability to listen with the head and heart is a crucial aptitude — the ultimate skill of a servant-leader. In fact, Robert Greenleaf believed that one must be a good listener in order to be a good servant-leader, and that listening alone can turn us into natural servants. Listening effectiveness grows when you listen from inside yourself, and when you approach what you are hearing with empathy for the speaker. Deep, active listening expands your world, makes you available for others and can produce changes for the speaker as well as the listener.

The Chinese have a symbol that portrays all the aspects of listening that a servant-leader employs — the ears, the eyes and the heart. The listener is present and gives undivided attention.

You

Eyes

Undivided Attention

Ear

Heart

Chinese Character "To Listen"

To read about listening is easy. Putting it into practice is more difficult. Fewer than two percent of us have had any formal training in listening skills. Below are some facts about listening that will help you understand why listening can be a difficult skill to master:

- Most people speak at 125-250 words per minute.
- We can accurately listen to a speech rate of about 400 words per minute, but we think at 1,000 to 3,000 words per minute. This creates a "listening gap."
- Immediately after hearing someone talk, we usually recall only about half of what we heard. Beyond that, we remember about 20% of what we hear.
- We are distracted, preoccupied or forgetful about 75% of the time.
- We spend about 45% of the time listening.

As the Chinese symbol for listening indicates, listening requires all of you — your eyes, your ears, your undivided attention and your heart. Some listening is done on the outside. Experts suggest that you practice **listening on the outside** by:

- Using appropriate eye contact. This can vary from culture to culture;
- Leaning forward slightly;
- Nodding your head;
- Avoiding distractions like the newspaper, television and phone calls;
- Not interrupting;
- Using encouraging phrases such as *I hear you, I see* and *tell me more*;
- Asking clarifying questions such as, *Are you saying that was very important to you?* and *What do you mean by that?*; and
- By paraphrasing what the other person has said and asking if you are correct in your understandings.

If most people just do these few things, those around them will notice the difference.

Listening takes a quantum leap when you listen from inside yourself and inside the speaker. Greenleaf describes **listening on the**

inside as being attentive to the inner voices and spirits of others.

Externalize the listening experience:
• Move into empathy by imagining yourself in the speaker's situation.
• Listen with your ears for the content and feeling.
• Listen from your heart and respond to the underlying emotion that the other person is trying to express without words. That emotion may or may not match the words the person uses.

Internalize the listening experience:
• Work on our own attitude.
• Use silence at times. Don't feel the need to "fill all the gaps."
• Avoid the temptation to apply a quick fix to the other person's problem.

We know that communication consists of more than just listening to words, it also involves **observing body language**. In *Some Uses of Nonverbal Expressions* (Group Learning Events, MATC Training Manual), Peggy Morrison writes:

> Nonverbal communication is a fact of life. It happens; it takes place. Consciously and unconsciously, we communicate with one another in nonverbal ways. It is not a question of having to learn something new because we have been doing it all our lives. What we express without words may give us real clues to our feelings, often clues which are not verbalized and may even put the lie to our verbalization. Becoming aware of how we communicate without words helps us to better send a message with congruence, words and nonverbal signals in harmony.

Listening Exercise

This listening exercise will give you and others the opportunity to practice "listening on the outside" through eye contact and encouraging phrases that demonstrate listening as well as "listening on the inside" through empathy and nonverbal expressions.

The exercise is a bit like the old "telephone" game in which one person whispers a message to the next person, who then whispers it to the next person and so on. The fun of that game is to see what happens to the original message as it is passed from one person to the next. The listening exercise has one individual share a story while one member of the group waits outside the room. The individual who waited outside then hears the story as told by those who just heard it. Finally, the story is retold to the original person — in a way that tries to honor the content and passion of the storyteller.

Ask the group to divide themselves up into teams of four. Assign roles A, B, C and D to the members of the team.

A = Person who shares
B = Empathetic listener one
C = Empathetic listener two
D = Observer

Round One (7 minutes)
1. **Persons A**, **B** and **D** are to remain in the room. **Person C** is to wait outside the room where he or she cannot hear the conversation.

2. **Person A** is to share a critical issue or challenge from work, or life in general, with which he or she is struggling at the present time. **Person A** is to share for five minutes. This is to be a time for authentic sharing rather than a time to resolve the issue. People should volunteer for this role.

3. **Person B** is to listen empathetically from both the outside and the inside. **Person B** will be conveying the information to **Person C**.

4. **Person D** will observe **Person B** and will later provide observations and feedback in *Round 4*.

Round Two (7 minutes)

1. **Person A** leaves the room. **Person C** enters the room and sits where Person A had been sitting.

2. **Person B** will now explain in five minutes as closely as possible both the feelings and the content of Person A's issue.

3. **Person C** is to listen from both the inside and the outside. Person C will be sharing what he or she heard from Person B.

4. **Person D** will listen, observe and later provide feedback to Person C.

Round Three (7 minutes)

1. **Person B** leaves the room. **Person A** returns and sits where Person B was sitting.

2. **Person C** will now share in five minutes with Person A what he or she learned about the critical issue that Person A originally shared. **Person A**, after listening from both the inside and the outside, is to indicate whether the statements being made are accurate.

3. **Person D** is to observe the interaction to provide feedback.

Round Four (30 minutes)

1. The **whole team of four** is to be in the room. The team is to reflect on the experience they just had, discussing what was easy and what was difficult, as well as feelings they had. What did it feel like to be listened to in this way?

2. **Person D** will talk specifically about his or her own feelings and experience of being a silent listener. Was it easier or more difficult to listen from the inside as the observer?

3. **Person D** will then provide specific feedback to each listener on what each did that was helpful and what might be more

helpful in future exchanges.

In the **large group**, process this experience by asking the following questions:

How was this experience different for you than previous listening experiences?

Was it easy or difficult for you to listen from both the inside and outside? Why?

What nonverbal behaviors did you observe?

What did you learn about listening? Capture these learnings on paper or a flip chart.

How can you apply these learnings in your work setting?

the gift of feedback

Feedback is communication relating information to a person or group about how certain behavior affects others. The purpose is to help individuals realize the impact of what they say or do, determining if the behavior matches their intent. It is an invitation and an opportunity for the receiver to change behavior that is problematic for others. For example, you may be in a conversation with someone who raises her voice with you. You assume she is angry with you based on your projection, which is the meaning you make of what you see or hear combined with your life experiences. In reality, the person in this case was raising her voice out of frustration that was not directed toward you. Providing feedback and being willing to receive feedback create opportunities to clarify situations that may otherwise be confusing or troubling for everyone involved.

Many times, we cringe when someone tells us that she or he needs to give us some feedback; we assume that what the other person is going to tell us will be critical, even hurtful. And when we need to deliver feedback, sometimes it's hard to figure out how to express ourselves in a way that produces constructive results. The good news is that it can be done, and this section will guide you in developing your own skills in giving and receiving feedback so that you can do both with confidence.

Tips for delivering **constructive feedback**:
- Begin with your perceptions of the behavior.
- Give a specific example.
- Explain clearly what effect the behavior has on you or others.

- Ask for change by stating the behavior you would prefer to see.

It is important when giving feedback to frame it positively so that the receiver does not become defensive.

Tips for delivering **positive feedback**:
- Give praise publicly; give criticism privately.
- Deliver it yourself, not through a third party.
- Share information rather than give advice.
- Avoid speculating on motives.
- Own your own feedback by using "I" rather than "you."
- Remember that you want to try to encourage positive future behavior.

Several factors affect how well feedback will be received, and, as most of us know, there is a right time and a wrong time to deliver feedback.

Tips for **well-timed feedback**:
- Time feedback so an individual or group won't be embarrassed.
- Give feedback when given the go-ahead to do so or when asked.
- Deliver feedback in time to prevent a serious mistake.

When it is time to give feedback, listening is just as important as talking.

Tips for **the feedback discussion**:
- Say less rather than more to start.
- Focus on what people actually said and did — use facts, numbers and examples.
- Listen and observe more often than act.
- Talk about what went well.
- Be sure the feedback involves an area that can be addressed.
- Don't give too much at once.
- Be sure you have been heard and understood.

It is just as important to receive feedback graciously as it is to deliver it graciously. Help the feedback giver feel confident that the feedback is well-received.

Tips for **receiving feedback**:
- Solicit feedback on your performance.
- Appear relaxed.
- Use positive, receptive body language such as nodding your head, and/or leaning forward.
- Make appropriate comments such as *I understand* and *I see your point*.
- Ask questions for clarification.
- Thank the giver for his or her time and input.

You can learn a great deal about how to give feedback if you reflect on the ways you like to receive it. As you think about how you best receive feedback consider **directness**, **timing**, **privacy**, **safety** and **content**.

Feedback Reflection Activity

Ask yourself the following questions:

What do you find most valuable to know?

Do you do anything that might inhibit people from giving you helpful feedback?

If you feel defensive when you receive certain feedback what could other people do to diffuse your feelings? If you get defensive, do you know why you have those feelings?

How can you suggest to others different ways of giving you feedback?

It is useful to see how the communication skills of active listening and feedback are used in the E-I-A-G Experiential Learning Cycle.

hearing: Hearing what is said by others is key to the communication skills of the servant-leader. The servant-leader by definition is intently interested in what others have to say, whether they are a client, customer, colleague or boss. It is important in listening to concentrate on hearing what is being said and not on thinking about what you want to say next. For example, as the identified person in an I-A-G reflection process, it is key to your learning to listen carefully and hear what others are saying about you.

active listening: Not all listening is active. You may "hear" what is being said but the speaker can only assume that you understood his or her meaning. Active listening is giving the speaker evidence of what you heard. In an I-A-G reflection process, the person whose behavior is being reflected upon gets a chance to listen to the effects of his or her behavior on others and an opportunity to share the learning that resulted from the listening.

clarifying questions: A part of listening includes clarifying what has been said rather than assuming the meaning. For example, if an I-A-G reflection process is being conducted on a statement that someone has made, the facilitator could ask, *When you say you were a 'mite upset,' do you actually mean you were very angry?*

probing questions: Probing questions are questions that elicit more pertinent data about what the speaker is saying. They not only can expand your perceptions and open you to new perspectives, they often enable the speaker to then elaborate on the original thought. The most effective probing questions are open-ended questions that begin with what or how. In the "analysis" portion of the I-A-G reflection process, probing questions, such as *When that happened, what did you think?* or *How did you feel?* are asked of participants and provide multiple perspectives. When you receive this type of data and are able to actively listen to the responses, you gain new insights into the effects of behavior.

giving and receiving feedback: Many people receive feedback more easily when it is delivered in a way that makes it easier to hear. One way to deliver feedback is to base it on the impact the behavior had on the person providing the feedback. In an I-A-G reflection process, individuals give feedback to the person whose behavior is being examined. The receiver may even ask for additional feedback to be given in the future so learning can continue beyond the present moment.

Lead me from death to life,
from falsehood to truth;
Lead me from despair to hope,
from fear to trust;
Lead me from hate to love,
from war to peace;
Let peace fill our heart,
our world, our universe.
Mother Teresa
The Joy in Loving

Trust also begets trust,
and confidence begets
confidence.
U Nu
first prime minister of Burma

The greatest compliment that
was ever paid to me was
when one asked me what I
thought, and attended to my
answer.
Henry David Thoreau

So when you are listening
to somebody, completely,
attentively, then you are
listening not only to the words,
but also to the feelings of what
is being conveyed, to the
whole of it, not part of it.
Jiddu Krishnamurti

Nature gave us one tongue
and two ears so we could
hear twice as much as we
speak.
Epictetus

Her finely-touched spirit had still its fine issues, though they were not widely visible. Her full nature ... spent itself in channels which had no great name on the earth. But the effect of her being on those around her was incalculably diffusive: for the growing good of the world is partly dependent on unhistoric acts; and that things are not so ill with you and me as they might have been, is half owing to the number who lived faithfully a hidden life, and rest in unvisited tombs.

George Eliot

Middlemarch

Listening rightly done is the most important thing you can do for a person.

Carl Rogers, Founder,

Client-Centered Therapy

On Becoming a Person

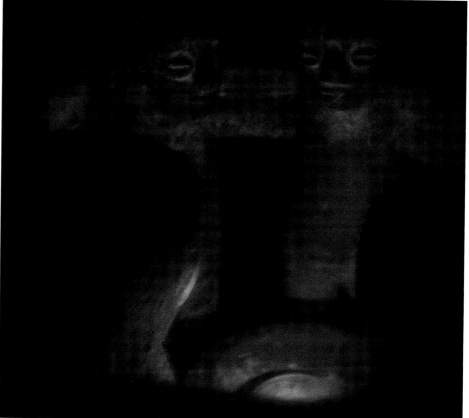

You think because you understand one you must understand two, because one and one makes two. But you must also understand 'and.'
Sufi Muslim teaching

When we gather in small groups, many dynamics shape our interactions with each other. In this section, we will examine trust, collaboration, shared decision making, power, group climate, effective meetings and disciplined reflection, all of which are crucial to the servant-leader journey.

the wealth of trust

trust *n*. **1:** Firm reliance on the integrity, ability, or character of a person or thing ... **2:** Something committed into the care of another; charge. **4 a:** The condition and resulting obligation of having confidence placed in one ... **b:** One in which confidence is placed. **5:** Reliance on something in the future; hope ...

Trust is the foundation upon which relationships are built. Servant-leaders understand that building relationships is at the core of nurturing those whom they serve. Being able to use the skills of listening, building consensus and helping individuals and communities grow all depend upon a foundation of trust.

Stephen Covey uses the metaphor of an **Emotional Bank Account** to describe the amount of trust that develops in a relationship. The idea suggests that every interaction with another person can be classified as a deposit or withdrawal into a "trust account." For example, deposits are made by showing kindness, keeping promises and making apologies. Withdrawals are the opposite. Demonstrating disrespect, breaking promises and being too proud to admit mistakes take away from a relationship. Withdrawals lessen trust in relationships while deposits build trust.

Trust Exercise

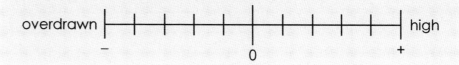

Complete the following exercise individually and then reflect upon your responses with a partner, if possible.

Think of a person whose relationship is important to you. Write that person's name here.

Place an X on the scale below to indicate your Emotional Bank Account balance with this person.

overdrawn |—|—|—|—|—|—|—|—| high

    −   0   +

What deposits can you make that would improve your level of trust in the relationship? Frame your answers from the other person's point of view. A deposit is only a deposit if the other person sees it that way.

Trust is the foundation for successful groups just as it is for successful one-on-one relationships. In a trusting group environment, individuals help each other not only to increase the level and quality of their performance, but also to help each other become better people. The **Jack Gibb Trust Formation** model helps explain the dynamics of group interactions and how group dynamics are based on trust:

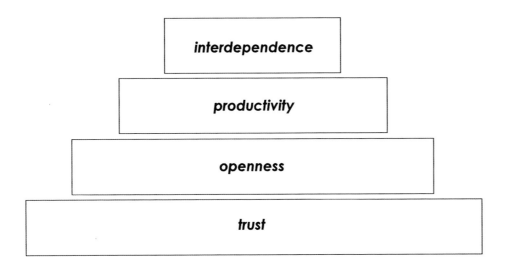

Jack Gibb Trust Formation

Each layer, or stage, depends upon the strength of the stage below it. Every group has the potential to increase the level of trust, openness, productivity and interdependence by resolving the primary concerns associated with each stage. When concerns at the lower levels of openness and trust are not addressed, a group can end up wounded and with diminished productivity. At this point, emphasizing productivity and interdependence will only exacerbate the situation.

Can I be myself? Who else is here? What is my role? Will I be heard? Acceptance is the basis of trust in a group. People often come to groups with unresolved feelings of fear and distrust. Unconsciously, group members ask themselves questions such as these concerning their level of acceptance in the group. These feelings sometimes are denied and often are rooted in a lack of acceptance of the self and consequent lack of acceptance of others. Individuals with these unresolved feelings are more concerned about membership in the group — how they might be heard, or whether they are important members — than in the group outcomes.

stages of trust formation

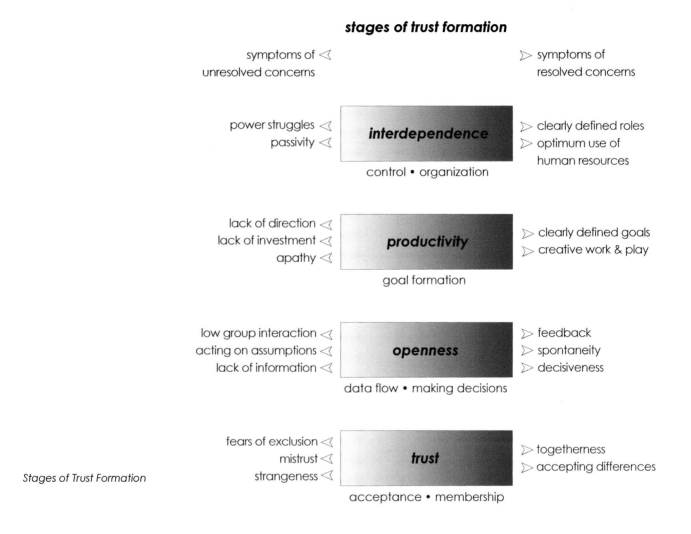

symptoms of ◁
unresolved concerns

▷ symptoms of
resolved concerns

power struggles ◁
passivity ◁

interdependence

▷ clearly defined roles
▷ optimum use of
human resources

control • organization

lack of direction ◁
lack of investment ◁
apathy ◁

productivity

▷ clearly defined goals
▷ creative work & play

goal formation

low group interaction ◁
acting on assumptions ◁
lack of information ◁

openness

▷ feedback
▷ spontaneity
▷ decisiveness

data flow • making decisions

fears of exclusion ◁
mistrust ◁
strangeness ◁

trust

▷ togetherness
▷ accepting differences

acceptance • membership

Stages of Trust Formation

How do I participate? What is your role? How does the group provide input? When the symptoms of unresolved concerns — fear of rejection or exclusion, mistrust or a sense of strangeness — are resolved, a sense of trust, togetherness and acceptance occurs. Within an effective group, members encourage openness about how people feel, how they perceive issues and listen to members' concerns for the group. If openness is not encouraged, there is little group interaction and members operate on assumptions rather than information. Mannerisms are cautious and polite to cover up true feelings and perceptions. This is exaggerated if group members have not gotten past the acceptance and membership stage. Information flow and decision making become laborious, fragmented and faulty.

What is our purpose? Where are we going? How will we measure results? When the group pauses to inquire about how people feel and think and draws on the expertise of members, the unresolved concerns around openness disappear. Data flow and decision making improve, and individuals work through their acceptance and membership needs in the process. Determining joint goals can be an early problem in groups. Goals often are imposed by individuals outside the group or by someone inside the group who wants it to go his way. Caution or politeness may prevent the group from reaching a clear sense of its goals. The group needs to engage in data flow again to try to reach a consensus on its goals before it can be productive. Group productivity is not a stage that is finally reached and maintained. The basic concerns from the lower level stages keep coming up and need to be addressed again and again.

Will I have influence? Can we work effectively together? People who have been able to integrate their many intrinsic goals into common goals show purposeful, meaningful and creative work leading to productivity. If goal formation has not been resolved, group members are unclear about how to exert control over their own impulses, internal forces or what happens in the group. Group members are at a loss as to how to organize what needs to be done. If individuals within the group have worked through acceptance, data flow and goal formation, they are more likely to be able to agree on member roles, leadership and how to organize to accomplish the group's goals.

When the group has resolved this fourth stage of trust formation, it will move beyond control issues to the optimum use of human resources — or true collegiality.

Members of a group can help the group move through the stages of trust and its potential by engaging in servant-leader behaviors: risking one's own self, accepting others' thoughts and feelings, listening, encouraging collaborative behavior, demonstrating openness and adopting a problem-solving attitude.

shared decision making

Shared decision making involves understanding and skill in the *Three C's*: **conflict**, **confrontation** and **collaboration**. All three are necessary for a servant-leader to be effective in helping groups make decisions. A group can make an effective decision by looking at the issue causing a conflict, using the skill of confrontation and collaboratively processing the issue.

CONFLICT | In a group, people's judgments and information naturally vary based on their backgrounds, values and perspectives. It is bringing these different perspectives together to make a group decision that most often yields better results than decisions made by a single individual. However, it is also because of different perspectives that there is always conflict on some level within a group. While conflict can be an outright confrontation, it can also be an internal awareness that all is not right. It occurs whenever a group or an individual is pulled by opposing forces that seem incompatible. There are different levels of conflict with which we deal daily, not all of which are potentially explosive. To handle conflict productively, individuals first need to understand on which level it is happening, because the *visible* conflict is not always the *true* source of tension.

The following diagram, frequently used by social scientists, illustrates how different sources of conflict operate at different levels. The upper levels of information, strategies and goals are more easily identified than those at lower levels. When conflict involving norms, values and beliefs occur, the reason for the conflict is not always known and it takes work to recognize and uncover the true source of the conflict before it can be managed appropriately.

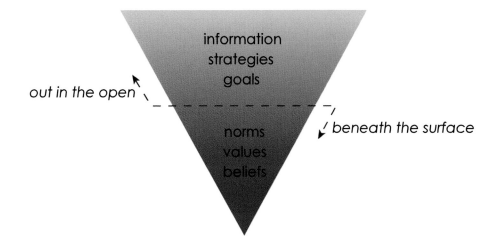

information
strategies
goals

out in the open

beneath the surface

norms
values
beliefs

Operating Levels for
Sources of Conflict

information: The group may be operating on a misunderstanding or lack of information. Conflicts here are the easiest to resolve by simply sharing and clarifying information.

strategies: Even if the group understands its goals, people may have different images and ideas of how to get there. Imparting information and negotiating a solution can help with strategy conflicts.

goals: These conflicts are related to what is to be done rather than how it is to be done. Listening to one another is key to resolving these types of conflicts.

norms: Norms are accepted behaviors by which a group operates and may or may not be stated. The group may not be aware that individuals are operating on different understandings of expected behaviors. While more difficult than upper-level conflicts, identifying and discussing group norms can help resolve these potential sources of contention.

values and beliefs: The group may not be aware that others hold basic truths at the core of their being differently. Individuals may be acting on values and beliefs that are different from others' values. Groups are more likely to engage in conflict at the higher levels of information, strategies and goals. When it is not clear what the conflict is about, it may be necessary to "dig down" one more level to look for the real source of conflict. It is not always possible to resolve differences in values and beliefs, and individuals may need to "agree to disagree."

Conflict may occur within oneself, between two people, within a group or between two groups. Servant-leaders **manage conflict** by:

- honestly exploring the true sources of conflict;
- asking questions and being willing to be changed by the answers;
- summarizing and restating positions;
- accepting persons even when disagreeing with positions;
- taking care that the group's highest needs are being served;
- looking for learning opportunities; and
- understanding that conflict is normal and expected when working in a group and helping others understand this to reduce anxiety and fear related to conflict.

Conflict Journaling

Think of a conflict situation you recently experienced. It either can be a conflict within yourself, or a conflict between you and another individual.

What was the visible conflict about and who was involved?

What do you believe was the real source of the conflict?

What might you have done to address the conflict if you had understood the source differently?

CONFRONTATION |

Most people do not welcome the thought of confronting others or being confronted. Yet conflict within ourselves and with others cannot be managed constructively until we deal with it. People avoid confrontations for two primary reasons:

- Not really knowing what they want, how they feel or what their values or priorities are; and
- Individuals may have learned that even if wants, needs and values are known, it is selfish or inappropriate to state them outright.

Being able to confront a situation, an individual or a group effectively with your feelings, wants or needs is the first step to addressing the conflict. Confronting an issue does not necessarily mean resolving it. There are benefits to simply talking about an issue that is bothering us. Once the concern is named, it often loses its energy and does not have to be held onto so tightly. By simply allowing someone to say what is bothering her, even though what she wants may not happen, she can often let it go and move on even if the outcome may be that she must continue to let it go rather than resolve the issue. Servant-leaders **engage in productive confrontation** by:

- developing skills for identifying wants based on feelings and values in any given situation. Servant-leaders understand the need to be aware of their emotions so as not to be controlled by them. It is also important to be clear about self-interests so that old behavior patterns are not automatically acted out;
- believing they actually deserve to have what they want;
- listening actively to others' feelings, values and wants, remembering that simply allowing someone to talk about an issue can eliminate the conflict without actually solving the problem; and
- being committed to resolving conflict by looking for "win-win" solutions, even if that may be an "agreement to disagree."

Think of a conflict situation you have experienced in which you avoided confrontation. Why did you avoid confronting the conflict?

Confrontation Journaling

If you believe there might be value in confronting the conflict, what strategies can you use to address the reason for avoiding the confrontation earlier?

Try discussing these strategies with a trusted friend or family member who may be able to help you clarify why you have difficulty in confronting this particular situation.

COLLABORATION | The diagram below from Stephen Covey's book, *The 7 Habits of Highly Effective People*, describes the degree of courage and consideration that exists in a relationship. The matrix describes the two dimensions as: (1) courage, the extent to which an individual attempts to satisfy her own concerns, and (2) consideration, the extent to which an individual attempts to satisfy the other person's concerns. Taking the various dimensions of the diagram together, we can identify four specific ways of dealing with conflict.

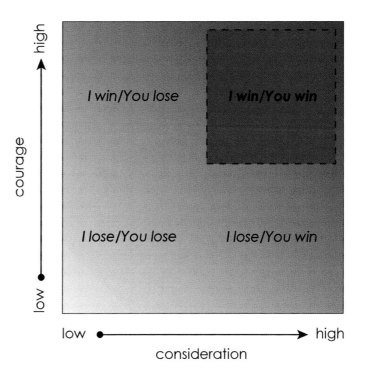

Courage vs. Consideration

by Steven Covey

Everyone is capable of using all **four conflict-handling modes**. However, people use some modes better than others based on their personal style and the particular situation and, therefore, tend to rely on those approaches to conflict handling more heavily. The modes are:

I win / You lose: might mean "standing up for your rights," defending a position that you believe is correct or simply trying to win. It can be useful in emergency situations when decisive action such as discipline or other issues vital to individual or group welfare are involved. While you may "win," causing the other individual or group to "lose" is detrimental to preserving a long-term relationship.

I lose / You win: might take the form of selfless generosity or charity, obeying another person's order even when it is in opposition to your own judgement or yielding to another's point of view. It can be useful in situations in which the issue is much more important to the other person than to yourself, when preserving harmony is especially important or when you realize you are wrong. Servant-leaders need to watch for potential overuse of this style. Yielding to another, while noble on occasion, can create resentment if your own wants and feelings are continually sacrificed.

I lose / You lose: might take the form of withdrawing or avoiding the conflict, or being so consumed with anger that one does not care if he loses as long as the other party loses as well. While avoiding the issue can be useful to let people cool down, or when the issue is not truly important to address, avoiding the discussion does not move the people involved forward in terms of resolving their concerns. The conflict can be left to fester, only to come out possibly at another time and probably with less control over emotions.

I win / You win: means cooperating with people to assure mutually beneficial, mutually satisfying agreements and solutions that allow all parties to get what they want. With a "win/win" solution, all parties feel good about the decision and committed to the plan of action. It is accomplished by identifying the underlying concerns of each party and trying to find an alternative that meets both sets of issues. The resulting decision is creative and high quality, commitment is high and the resources of all group members have been incorporated.

Collaboration works well when both sets of concerns are too important to be compromised, to merge insights from people with different perspectives on a problem, to work through hard feelings that have been interfering with an interpersonal relationship and to gain commitment by incorporating various considerations into a consensual decision.

The "win/win" approach can also be described as **consensus decision making**. The consensus approach is a process in which each group member or each party has had adequate and fair input into the discussion to influence the decision that is made. It is important to remember, however, that consensus does not mean unanimous support of a particular decision. It means each member of a group has had the opportunity to influence the decision of the group. The decision may not be viewed by individual members as their "preferred" choice, but they can live with the decision and can advocate and implement it. True consensus and collaboration requires a great deal of thought, trust, exploration, mutual support and time. Servant-leaders **engage in collaboration and consensus behaviors** by:

- actively soliciting and exploring others' ideas and positions as well as their own;
- taking the time to make sure language and wording are clear;
- helping others clarify and develop their own view points;
- allowing others to help clarify and develop their own viewpoints; and
- testing that the issue has been addressed or resolved for everyone, as satisfaction for one person does not necessarily equal resolution of the issue for the other person

Consensus decision making strikes a balance between courage and consideration, and servant-leaders strive for developing a personal predisposition for this approach.

Collaboration Exercise

Divide the group into teams of five to eight. Allow 15 minutes to discuss the following scenario. If time allows, have the group conduct an E-I-A-G on a significant learning moment that occurred during its discussion.

You are a neighborhood group which must agree on the use of an abandoned warehouse that borders the neighborhood. The facilitator may assign roles that create conflict such as the historical society chair, the local priest, the corporate representative, the teen center advocate and the parents of young children.

How were conflict and confrontation used?

Was the group able to agree on a solution?

What type of conflict-handling model(s) did the group use?

Review the skills and theories of trust, collaboration and decision making. Explain that teams now will have the opportunity to put these skills into practice on a second task and to explore the differences among the various approaches.

Give each team two pieces of newsprint or flipchart paper, a stack of straws (16-20), masking tape and an egg.

Each team is to build a structure with only these materials that will keep the egg from breaking when the structure and egg are dropped from 6 feet.

The group members will have 10 minutes to plan before they touch the material. At the sound of the bell, they then will be given 15 minutes to build the structure.

The structures then will be tested.

List the following questions and ask each team to consider these as it reflects on its experience.

What was done to make sure data flowed concerning the task?

How were goals or targets set in each case?

Did conflict arise about what was expected? How was it addressed?

Were there issues around power in the group? How were these handled?

How was the diversity of the team used?

power and servant-leadership

An honest desire to serve others is an integral part of being a servant-leader. It does not mean giving up one's own needs or desires. Rather it means using one's personal power for the good of all. Having the desire to serve is essential and needs to be coupled with skills and awareness to prevent others from being discounted or hurt in the process of working and living together.

In addition to their personal power, servant-leaders are granted power because of who they are as persons and how they act in the interests of others. It is important not to confuse appropriate use of power with simply controlling others, which can be as simple as telling people what to do and making sure they do it through punishments and rewards.

While on the surface this may seem simpler and more efficient, studies as far back as social scientist Douglas McGregor's 1960's *X and Y Theory* tell us that people will work better, longer and be happier when they are treated with respect and their input is acknowledged and appreciated. With the exception of some emergency situations in which the most knowledgeable person needs to take control, shared power leads to better involvement and productivity.

Serving others is more complicated than wielding control. It is a lifelong process connected to our own growth and maturity. That lifelong process includes how to develop our own power and how to use it ethically.

Answer the following questions individually or as a group.

What are some positive and negative associations we make with the word "power?"

How do you contrast sharing power with exercising power over others?

How do you know when people are powerful?

Whom would you describe as powerful and how is their power exercised?

What do they have, or do, that others do not?

What do you think their attitudes are toward others?

What do you think the images these people have of themselves would be?

Do the responses to the above questions describe individuals who are perceived to have power based on their position or money?

Or do the examples identify individuals who are perceived to have power based on their integrity?

PERSONAL POWER |

Janet Hagberg, in her work *Real Power: Stages of Personal Power in Organizations*, provides us with a model that analyzes the evolution of personal power. As you read through the model, remember that all of us can bounce around among the stages, sometimes during the same day. The problem arises when we get stuck in one stage that prevents us from being servant-leaders.

Hagberg reminds us that people can be leaders at any stage of personal power. Stages four and above best illustrate the qualities of a servant-leader.

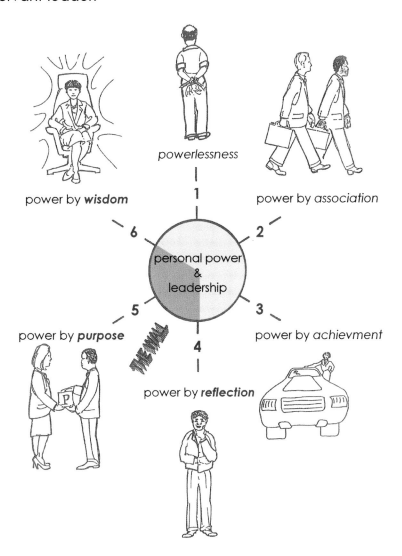

Personal Power and Leadership

by Janet Hagberg

GROUP FUNCTIONS |

Even when there is no designated leader, power exists within and among individual group members. In their early work, human behavioral theorists Kenneth D. Benne and Paul H. Sheats looked beyond the leader to understand how each member's functions and behaviors contribute to group effectiveness. They theorized that it is the combined functions of leader and group members that is essential and determines overall group growth and production. They organized the functions into three catagories: **Group Task Functions**, **Group Building and Maintenance Functions** and **Individual Functions**. When Group Maintenance and Task Functions are being addressed, the energy of the group is better focused. Equally true, when each individual's contributions are valued, a healthy relationship grows between individual and group needs, and members are focused on performing the task. The Benne and Sheats categories are illustrated in the diagram below; The Gabriel Center refers to this concept as the Group, Individual, Task (GIT) Theory:

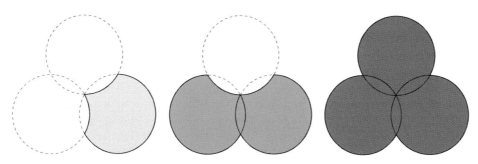

Interdependence of
GIT Functions

In order for each GIT function to be fulfilled, all must be addressed.

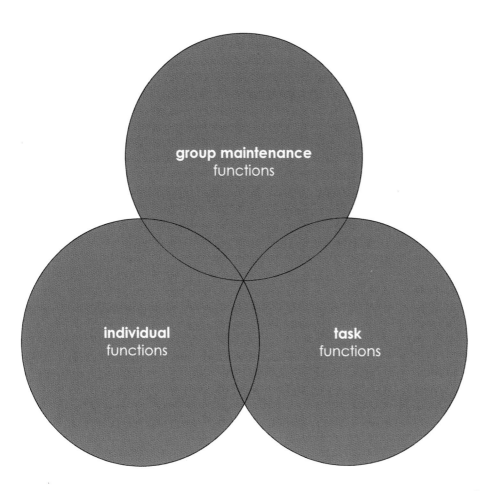

The GIT Model

This diagram outlines the healthy behavioral functions in each of the three areas of the GIT model that enhance group development from a servant-leader perspective. The "G" and "T" circles are basically the same set of behaviors described in Benne and Sheats' work. However, they specified the "I" roles and behaviors that satisfy individual, personal needs and do not necessarily contribute to the group's accomplishing its goals. Examples of such behavior include being the aggressor, blocker, recognition seeker, self-confessor, disrupter, dominator, help-seeker or special interest leader. Sometimes aggressive, dominating or blocking behaviors may occur when an individual feels that her contributions are not being valued. The GIT model here emphasizes the "I" roles and functions that do foster group accomplishment, particularly when the meeting or gathering of the group is being facilitated according to the servant-leader model. It is important to keep the "G" and "T" functions balanced. For example, when group members focus entirely on task functions, individual contributions can be overlooked, people may not feel heard or valued and they can withdraw their energy from other members and the task, and the group and its goals will suffer.

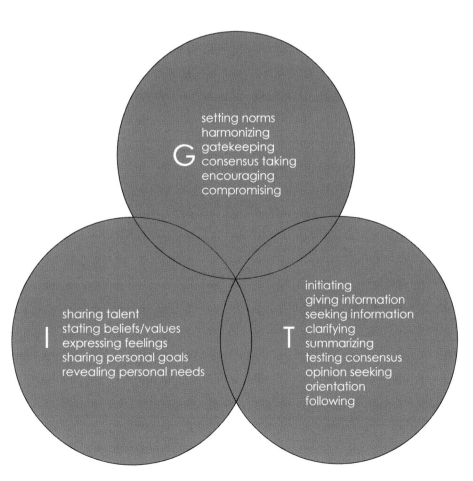

Healthy Behavioral Functions

in the GIT Model

Just as sunshine, rain, wind and snow combine to form an overall weather climate, individual behaviors combine to form a group climate. We tend to know more about the weather than group processes. The following chart can help us learn more about the group climate.

*these **behaviors*** ➡ *create this **climate*** ➡ *with these **responses***

controlling
punishing
regulating
telling   **defensive**
shaming
guilt-producing
judging

conforming
resenting
depending
avoiding initiative
hiding & denying
apathy & depression
deception

listening
understanding
trusting
sharing   **accepting**
clarifying
rewarding

experimenting
creating
exposing
autonomy
participating
producing

Group Behaviors, Climate

& Responses

Have a group discussion about what each of you would do if you were observing any of the defensive behaviors, or the corresponding responses, in a group or team in which you were working or facilitating.

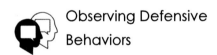

Observing Defensive Behaviors

Groups have a tendency to develop patterns of behaviors, while various group members contribute according to their abilities and their psychological state at any one time. As stated earlier, when any of the GIT functions are over- or under-used, the group is out of balance and effectiveness will suffer. It is very important to be able to identify the different functions so that the lack of the appropriate function can be addressed to realign the group. The following exercise can be used to practice identifying GIT functions.

Form two groups of five to eight people in Groups A and B. Group A sits in a circle, with participants facing each other. Group B forms a larger circle surrounding Group A, so that the

Fishbowl Exercise

people in Group B can see the people in Group A. Group A is assigned a simple task, such as agreeing on where to have a party, deciding on a menu, picking a special event to attend or selecing a name for your group that requires consensus within a specified time (10-12 minutes).

Optional: Some Group A participants can be given secret instructions to focus on using a particular function described in the GIT model.

Each Group B member is assigned to observe a Group A member who can be seen from across the group. After the task is completed the Group B member will give feedback to the individual he was observing and describe the functions in which the Group A member was engaged.

Group A is asked to stop the task at the end of specified time, even if the task has not been completed.

effective meetings

Statistics tell us that people spend an inordinate amount of time in meetings. Some of the complaints about meetings are: *There are too many meetings, Most meetings are a waste of time, No one listened to what I had to say, I had too much on my mind to focus on the meeting,* or *The meeting was poorly run.*

All of these complaints are true at times and meetings should be called when necessary. Sometimes meetings are important because bringing individuals together leads to the synergy that promotes good ideas and provides opportunities to strengthen relationships.

Many of the complaints that people have about such experiences can be avoided if meetings are well run and people feel they are worth their time. There is no shortage of material on how to run effective meetings by using meeting tools and evaluating how well tasks are performed. While this type of material can help manage the task portion of meetings, it does not address how to manage the relationship portion of meetings. The Gibbs Trust Formation Model, discussed earlier, identifies trust and openness as the foundation of effective group interaction. Symptoms of unresolved trust and obstacles to openness include fear of rejection, operating on assumptions and being polite to cover up true feelings and perceptions. When the group pauses to inquire about how people feel and think, these unresolved concerns disappear and trust, acceptance and understanding begin to form.

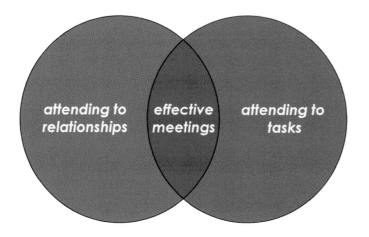

The following meeting guidelines emphasize the importance of balancing both the task and the relationship side of meetings:

getting on board: Begin the meeting by suggesting that group members share thoughts that could be distracting or having a negative impact upon their participation in the meeting. It is amazing how being allowed to say what is preventing one from being present allows the person to then set the distraction aside for the moment.

Some groups prefer a more active way of coming together and could choose to do one of the icebreakers below. To be most helpful, the choice should depend on the history of the group together and the desired outcomes of the community building and data flow that would arise from the time spent in reflection. You may share with the group the following:

- a recent positive experience
- a piece of wisdom you have learned
- the best characteristics of a mentor you know
- your most common excuse
- one of your strongest qualities
- an award or recognition you have received
- the best and worst advice you have ever received

reflection: Following the "Getting On Board" question, it can be very useful to allow a minute or two for quiet reflection time for participants to get centered prior to beginning task work. Selected readings, quotations, artwork, music or a "check-in question" can be incorporated very effectively.

task at hand: Now participants are better prepared to deal with the items and decisions that necessitated the meeting being called. The group may be accustomed to having the same leader (chairperson or facilitator), a recorder, a time-keeper; making decisions by consensus or following Robert's Rules of Order. Whatever the model, it is critical that each individual's contributions be acknowledged. Having an agenda prepared in advance and sticking to the agenda is important. However, as we demonstrate in the *Using Disciplined Reflection in Meetings: Group Activity Sample Script*, being willing to stop the process and reflect on a critical incident strengthens understanding among members and promotes future working relationships.

how did we do?: Evaluating how the meeting went is very important. Servant-leaders always want to learn from what happens and make improvements for next time. A quick, simple, yet very effective method of doing this is called the **Plus-Delta model**.

Plus-Delta Evaluation

Copy the Plus-Delta graphic below on a piece of chart paper so that everyone can see. Ask participants to express first what went well during the meeting in the (+) column. Then ask participants to express what they believe could be changed for the better in the (Δ) column. Again, comments should be written on the chart paper. These comments can lead to a brief discussion of how the group can change and improve the next meeting. In some instances, a particular Delta comment can lead to a disciplined reflection, *E-I-A-G*, for deeper learning.

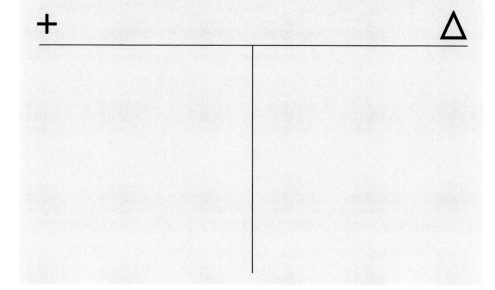

It is important to remember that people have different ideas about how meetings should be conducted; therefore, it is critical that everyone knows what meeting style will be used before the meeting begins. This can eliminate a great deal of energy being wasted by people wondering *What's going on here?* or thinking *We should be doing this a different way.*

For a bit of fun, you can think of the guidelines for effective meetings outlined here as "Roberta's Rules of Order," as distinguished from the traditional "Robert's Rules of Order" mentioned above. Although both models are designed to help groups accomplish their goals, they go about it in different ways. With "Robert's Rules of Order," the parliamentary process is the authority in how the meeting will be conducted, and sessions working according to this procedure can feel controlled and overly focused on efficiency.

| ROBERTA'S RULES OF ORDER

With "Roberta's Rules of Order," the people attending the meeting are considered to be the authorities, along with the facilitator. As you lead a group with the guidelines described in this chapter, you will find that the meeting has a more open feel, with more space for the members to participate in a less controlled way.

Any means you can find to send the message to the group that the meeting is theirs, not yours alone, will enhance their investment in the work and their eagerness to help the task to be accomplished. So, for example, if you prepare an agenda beforehand, you can send it to the group members and ask them to add to it; you can also check with them again in the meeting to see if there are any changes.

In addition, as often as it seems reasonable, you can invite the group to share in basic decisions: where to meet, when, for how long. The group can decide before beginning the agenda how long it expects to spend on each item; then when the time-keeper says that the time is up for that piece on the agenda, the group can decide whether to keep discussing it or move on. It is, however, important, to be intentional about bringing any leftover items forward to the next meeting so that they do not linger too long on the "to do" list.

Another way to foster healthy groups is to ask a member to be the "values keeper" during the meeting who then can point out times when she or he sees servant-leadership happening and make the others aware of it.

The servant-leader, in putting these guidelines to use, will also demonstrate to the group one of the most powerful tenets of servant-leadership — a leader manifesting strength by letting go of unilateral contro — and the creativity, joy, productivity and just basic fun that can bloom in the space created by that loosening of the grip.

experiencing and facilitating disciplined reflection

Servant-leaders use disciplined reflection to enhance the effectiveness of meetings and other group activities. Bringing to the surface the data that are not always stated in a group, or even the data that are in the group's collective unconscious, can enable the members to function in a transparent and open fashion. Assumptions can be tested, disagreements can be understood and even disruptive behavior can be managed. At the group level the effect of behavior can become part of the data available to the members of the group. The E-I-A-G disciplined reflection process can be most useful in expanding individual and group awareness of behavior, which in turn allows the group to be more productive, as it can encourage members to continue helpful behavior and change disruptive behavior. The following is a step-by-step application for your group:

step 1: The facilitator begins by reminding the group members that they have been having a "group experience" since they gathered together. This Experience is the "E" in the E-I-A-G experiential learning cycle.

step 2: The facilitator then asks: *What has occurred in this group since we convened that arouses your curiosity and about which you want to learn more? What happened that had some emotional impact on you or seemed to affect the group?* This focus on a specific piece of behavior or activity is the Identification part of the I-A-G reflection process. It is the piece of the experience to be analyzed. If no one in the group volunteers any incidents, the facilitator may suggest one that seemed to affect the group. The reflection is most productive if the action focused on is as specific as possible. Someone's actions or comments are often most appropriate. Similar to a hologram, a picture that when turned just the right way in the light reveals its three-dimensional form, disciplined reflection focuses on a small portion of the group activity and reveals a holistic picture of the group dynamics.

step 3: If the behavior — actions or words — of an individual is involved, the facilitator then asks that individual if it is all right to focus on her. (That individual will be referred to as Louise in this description.) Louise probably has the most to learn as an individual. However, it is not appropriate to proceed without her permission.

step 4: If Louise agrees to proceed with the reflection process, the facilitator then asks her to remain silent while the facilitator elicits the thoughts, feelings and actions of others during the incident involving Louise. Members of the group are asked the questions: *What did you think when the incident occurred? What were your feelings? What did you do?* Most of the responses to these questions are data that have not been available to the group. This is the first part of the Analysis in the I-A-G reflection process.

step 5: The facilitator then can continue the analysis by checking assumptions that group members might have had. The question can be asked directly: *What assumptions did you have about individuals and their actions?*

step 6: The facilitator continues the analysis by determining what the effect of the incident was on the group. The question posed can be as straightforward as, *What was the effect of the incident on the group?*

step 7: The facilitator then turns to Louise and elicits the data about her intentions when she spoke or acted in the way she did.

step 8: To assist Louise in learning more about herself from the data heard from others and analyzed to this point, the facilitator asks the following: *What insights did you gain about yourself or the* *group? What does this mean for you in the future? What would you do differently next time?* This is the first part of the Generalize step of the I-A-G reflection process.

step 9: The facilitator then asks others in the group what their learnings are about the group or themselves. Questions can be asked such as: *Will some of you share your learnings about yourselves or the group? What does this mean for the future?*

Now that you have learned how a group can benefit from an E-I-A-G, here's a quick guide to follow when performing your own group E-I-A-G.

E Experience
A group experience in which the entire group has participated.

I Identify
The facilitator asks the following questions to the group:

What has occurred in the group experience about which you wish to learn more?
What is a specific behavior or activity for the focus of the I-A-G?
Do you all recall this incident?
(It is important that everyone recalls the incident.)

The facilitator then addresses an individual, if the focus is on that individual:

Are you willing to have the group focus on you?
(If the individual does not wish to be the focus of the I-A-G, another should be chosen.)
Since we are focusing on you, please simply listen until we hear others' reactions.

 Analyze
The facilitator asks the following questions to the group:

What were you thinking when the incident occurred?
What were your feelings?
What did you do?
What assumptions are you making?
What was the effect of the incident on the group?

The facilitator then addresses the individual:

What were your intentions?

Generalize

The facilitator then asks the following questions to the group:

What did you learn from this reflection about yourself or working in groups?
What insights did you gain?
What applications do you see for the future?

Finally, the facilitator address the individual:

What did you learn about groups?
What insights did you gain?
What applications do you see for the future?

In this activity, you will experience how an E-I-A-G can be put into action while leading a group.

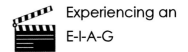
Experiencing an
E-I-A-G

Samuel and Teresa are co-leaders of an annual membership meeting held by a servant-leader association. Samuel and Teresa were given the responsibility to plan the meeting that was to be attended by 50 members from many different parts of the country. During the business meeting shortly before lunch, the members heard a presentation of the financial report, and then the following exchange took place.

Fred: [white male] These figures are appalling. How did we get into such a financial mess? If we'd had stronger leadership, this wouldn't have happened.

| Experience

Yvonne: [black female] That sounds like an attack on our president, Mary. I believe that if the president were a white male instead of a black female, he would have had more support, and we wouldn't have such a negative financial report.

Samuel, as co-leader, hesitated a few seconds to consider how he, as a white male, might handle this situation. Louise immediately stood up and came to the front of the group.

Louise is a white female who has extensive experience and an impeccable reputation as a diversity facilitator.

Louise: [to Samuel and the group] I think we should deal with the issue in front of us right now. We always sweep it under the rug. I can lead a diversity exercise that will help us gain greater understanding in addressing what is happening in our group.

Teresa: [to Louise and the group] I understand your wanting to help us. There is clearly tension in the room. However, I think that before we do the diversity exercise, it is important to stop and reflect on what has just happened. If we bring to our awareness some of the dynamics in the group, we will be better able to decide on our next steps — including your leading a diversity exercise.

The servant-leaders were used to this kind of disciplined reflection to help gain a greater understanding of group dynamics, so with the group's agreement, Teresa proceeded to facilitate an I-A-G.

Identify |

Teresa: [to the group] We have all experienced the presentation of the financial report and a number of responses and actions that followed. Let's identify a focus for our reflection.

Myriam: I think we should focus on Fred's comment.

Alex: Yvonne's response to Fred was pretty important.

Sariel: I believe that we could learn from both of these; however, I was most affected when Louise stepped to the front of the group.

Teresa: [to Sariel and the group] You are right, Sariel; we could learn from any of these possibilities that have now been mentioned. We have usually found that if we pick one of them, the data will flow. I suggest that we focus on Louise's stepping in front of the group and what she said. If that doesn't add enough clarity, we can focus on one or both of the other identifications.

Teresa: [to Louise] Before we begin, let me check with you to see if you are willing to have the group focus on your actions in an I-A-G.

Louise: [to Teresa] I guess that would be okay. I was just offering to help us work through an issue that obviously needs to be addressed.

Teresa: [to Louise] Remember that you probably have the most to learn from the reflection process.

Louise: [to Teresa and the group] I know. Let's do it.

Teresa: [to Louise] As usual, we will ask you to listen without speaking until we hear the reactions of others.

Teresa: [to the group] Let's be clear about the specific experience that we are identifying as the focus of our analysis and learning. What were the behavior, actions and words that occurred in that moment?

Sariel: My recollection is that Louise stood up, came forward to the front of the room and said something like, "I can lead an exercise that will help us understand what is happening."

Myriam: I heard her also say that we always sweep this issue under the rug and that we should deal with it right now.

Teresa: That fits with my memory. Louise stood up, came forward and said that we should deal with this issue as it was in front of us at the time, instead of sweeping it under the rug. She then offered to lead an exercise to gain greater understanding to address the issue. Is the focus of the I-A-G clear?

Teresa: Put yourself back in the moment when Louise stood up and came forward and addressed the group. Do you all recall that moment? (Pause) What were your thoughts when this occurred?

Sariel: I thought we were in a difficult situation. I wasn't sure whether to support what Louise suggested or not.

Myriam: I, too, was ambivalent. I think the issue that was raised by Yvonne is of vital importance.

Alex: I thought that since Louise is such a competent diversity trainer, she could really help us out.

Samuel: A flood of thoughts came into my head when Louise came forward. I know how competent she is. I began to question whether I could continue facilitating effectively. I was fully aware of how important the issue that Yvonne had raised is to us, but most of all I was concerned about the agenda. After all, we had put a lot of effort into figuring out how to provide time for everything we need to do, and I wasn't sure how we could fit anything this major into the schedule. I was aware of how very important I think it is that we address the recommendations regarding answering the challenges involved in our financial situation.

Teresa: Any additional, different thoughts?

Sue: [to Teresa] I'm glad you asked; my head was in a different place when Louise stepped forward. I was thinking about a luncheon date I have, and I was concerned that Louise's exercise would run right through our break time. I was feeling hungry and frustrated.

Teresa: Thanks for your thoughts and feelings, Sue. Let's hear others' feelings.

Samuel: My feelings were annoyance.

Teresa: Annoyance at Louise?

Samuel: Yes, in fact it was probably stronger than annoyance, probably anger. I was feeling personally diminished since it seemed as if Louise were hijacking the agenda.

Teresa: Thanks for acknowledging your anger, Samuel. Any other feelings?

Alex: I was excited when Louise suggested doing the exercise. I want to understand the issue.

Yvonne: I felt hopeful that we would really deal with the issue of effective leadership and how we create, or don't create, the conditions for leadership to flourish.

Sariel: My feelings were ones of confusion. I want to support Samuel, and I want to support Louise.

Fred: I was scared. I wasn't sure if my intentions would be understood in Louise's exercise. I really am concerned about our leadership in the organization.

Teresa: [to Fred] Let's stay focused on what Louise did for now, Fred. The I-A-G works better if we stay focused. So my understanding is that you were scared about your intentions not being understood. Is that right?

Fred: Yes, that's right. And I can wait and raise the leadership issue later.

Teresa: Any other thoughts and feelings to add to the analysis? (Pause) Hearing no more different thoughts and feelings, what did any of you do when Louise stepped forward?

Samuel: [to Teresa] Well, I looked at you because I didn't know what to do. I'm glad we're now reflecting on that moment.

Teresa: [to the group] Any other actions in response to Louise's stepping forward? (Pause) It seems that we can continue the analysis. What assumptions were you making about others?

Alex: I was assuming that Samuel wasn't up to the task of facilitating the group at that point in time.

Yvonne: I assumed that Samuel's hesitation was because he didn't want to deal with racial content. I don't believe that now.

Teresa: Any additional assumptions? (Pause) If not, let's turn to Louise and see what her intentions were when she stepped up to the front of the room.

Louise: My intentions were to be helpful to the group. I really think that I can lead the group in an exercise that will help us to gain understanding about the racial tension we are experiencing. However, after hearing the others respond, I realize that my intervention created more reaction than I expected. There always seem to be other perspectives that aren't immediately obvious.

Teresa: [to Louise] It sounds as though you are already drawing learnings from this reflection on what you did. Before you look at what you learned, what do you think was the effect on the group of your stepping forward?

Louise: We can see that different people responded in very different ways. Since we stopped to do an I-A-G, we don't know what would have happened if we hadn't taken the time for reflection just then. However, now I think we are ready to make a more informed decision about how to proceed.

Teresa: I think we should close off the I-A-G with our learnings about ourselves or the group.

Teresa: [to Louise] Why don't you continue with your statement of what you have learned?

Louise: I think I acted somewhat impulsively since I care so much about resolving the racial tension. I've learned that when I act impulsively on my passion, my intention to help may be lost in the strong reactions.

Teresa: [to Louise] What might you do in the future?

Louise: I think I would check in with the designated facilitator before taking on the role of facilitator myself. In fact, that is what I would like to do right now.

Teresa: [to Louise] Let's hold that for just a minute while we finish the I-A-G reflection process and give the other members of the group an opportunity to draw learnings.

Louise: [to Teresa] Okay.

Sariel: I learned once again how many different thoughts and feelings are in the room at any point in time. It is awesome. I'm glad we took the time to process this incident.

Samuel: [to Teresa] I learned how important it is to have co-leaders for these meetings. I just couldn't respond quickly enough to continue facilitating the meeting in an effective way. I'm certainly pleased you were right here with me and involved in the situation.

Fred: I often act impulsively just like Louise was saying. In the future, I will be aware that acting impulsively and with passion may raise reactions that will block my intentions.

Yvonne: After hearing the processing, I am beginning to believe that this organization is ready to deal more deeply with the way we support our black leadership.

Alex: I'm beginning to understand how really difficult it can be to facilitate this group. I'm surely glad we know how to I-A-G.

Teresa: Are there other learnings? We may not have time to hear all of them, but if you have one you want to share, please do. (Pause) Thanks for taking the time for disciplined reflection; I think we have the information to move forward now with greater clarity.

Following the reflection process, the group immediately decided to have Teresa, Samuel and Louise meet over lunch to see how the agenda could accommodate both addressing the financial situation and also dealing with the issues raised about leadership and the way in which people of color are supported in their roles.

Now it is time for you to coach others in facilitating the disciplined reflection. Any member of a group can stop the action and see what individuals can learn about themselves and the group from what has happened. It is one experience to participate in the E-I-A-G disciplined reflection; it is another actually to facilitate an I-A-G. From what we know about adult learning, facilitating the I-A-G is the best way to learn how to do it.

In the following scenario, you will be helping Samuel learn to facilitate an I-A-G.

step 1: Note a time in the life of the group for learning – a time when a disciplined reflection would reveal valuable learning. The best time for a reflection might be right after the most recent session of the group, since there are always experiences the group can I-A-G. Or the next time might be at a point during the session when an episode occurs from which the learning looks particularly valuable. For example, action could be stopped for disciplined reflection when confusion or tension arises or when the group appears to be blocked.

step 2: You as the coach pick the Experience that is the period of time from which the group will identify a particular behavior for the focus of the I-A-G. Sometimes it is quite clear which span of time to choose for the Experience. Some groups make it a practice to set aside time at the end of each meeting for using the I-A-G to process their time together. Sometimes the circumstances surrounding a conflict or a time of high emotion are chosen. It is important that the Experience be a common time for all those who will participate in the I-A-G. Usually it is easiest to learn if the time is quite recent.

step 3: Now it is time for the Identification part of the I-A-G. Since you are helping Samuel learn to facilitate the I-A-G, you might have Samuel use chart paper in front of the group to record the steps of the I-A-G. Using chart paper to list possible incidents for the focus of the I-A-G provides a way to begin keeping a visual record of the I-A-G and the steps involved in it. The Identification step is crucial because choosing a particularly specific behavior for the focus enhances the I-A-G process and the learnings that result from it. You can help Samuel by making sure that he knows the importance of the group's choosing a specific comment or action during the common experience.

step 4: At this point, Samuel's task is to help the group select one of the specific incidents in the Identification step. Ordinarily you want to choose the incident that would provide the most powerful learning for the group or an individual member. However, for the purpose of learning to facilitate the I-A-G, it is easiest to pick a simple action of one person that had an impact on the group. Have Samuel ask the group to name various incidents on which to focus while he lists them on the chart paper. Then have Samuel ask the group members to indicate by a show of hands which incident they would like to I-A-G. This determines where the energy of the group resides. Then it is important for Samuel to ask the individual whose action has been identified whether it is OK to focus on that person and his action. If not, another incident is chosen.

step 5: Once the specific incident has been chosen, remind Samuel to check to be sure that everyone remembers the incident. It usually helps to have someone repeat the words that were used or describe the action taken in the identified moment. Have Samuel remind the person who initiated the incident to remain a listener only and not engage in the conversation until the reactions of others are noted first.

step 6: The first part of the Analysis is soliciting the thoughts, feelings and actions of others in response to the incident. It usually is easier to solicit thoughts than feelings. Have Samuel use the chart paper in front of the room as a continuation of the I-A-G's visual record. Making separate lists for thoughts, feelings and actions helps clarify the responses. The separate list of thoughts and feelings is also useful in helping group members distinguish between their thoughts and feelings. It may be necessary to probe for feelings, since many people are less able to recognize and describe their feelings than they are able to identify and express their thoughts.

step 7: Continuing with the Analysis, support Samuel as he checks for any assumptions that were made by members of the group by encouraging him to note the group's assumptions on chart paper and thereby continuing the visual record of the I-A-G. By this time, there may be data reported by others indicating that these assumptions were not accurate.

step 8: The final part of the data from the group is to identify the effect of the behavior on the group. This part of the Analysis should be based on data observed or brought to the surface by the reflection process. As you coach Samuel, help him to bring clarity to the statements being made without adding his own interpretation.

step 9: Now it is time to return to the person whose behavior is being analyzed. Up to this point, this individual has remained quiet in order to listen and check his own intentions when the incident occurred. Here it is important to help the person from becoming overly defensive. Help Samuel encourage clear statements of intention together with thoughts and feelings at the time of the intervention.

step 10: Samuel then helps individuals check to see whether, having heard the intent of the person whose behavior is being examined, any of their assumptions have changed. It is also useful to see if the person central to the incident has made or changed any assumptions.   .

step 11: Before moving on to discover what group members have learned through the reflection process, an additional connection can be made at a different level. You can coach Samuel to ask questions such as: "Were you aware of an intangible, unseen force, energy, power or spirit present with us during the moment that we have just analyzed or during the reflection process itself?" "What more can you say about that?" Or, with a faith community, you can ask: "Does this incident remind you of any episode in your faith heritage, whether from your oral tradition or in your sacred text such as the Koran, Torah or Bible?" This connection with the spiritual level or perspectives of a faith community then becomes a part of the reflection process in order to enhance the learning.

step 12: Now it is time to report learnings. The person central to the identified moment reports first. Here the coaching of Samuel needs to focus on making sure this person stays with his own learnings rather than focusing on what other people have said during the I-A-G so far. Again, it is important to keep defensiveness to a minimum.

step 13: The final step is to ask others to share their learnings from the incident and the reflection process. Encourage Samuel to acknowledge when learnings seem to be contradictory. Since each person is reporting his or her own truth, the learnings do not all have to fit together.

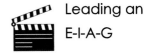 Leading an
E-I-A-G

At the end of a stressful but fruitful day at the annual meeting of a servant-leader association with members coming from different parts of the country, the planning team was reflecting on the day's work in order to enhance its own learning about facilitating such gatherings. Samuel and Teresa were part of the planning team as the co-leaders for the annual meeting. The other members of the planning team were Angela, George and Kwame. Here is some dialogue from that meeting of the planning team:

Samuel: [co-leader] Wow. This is my first time as a leader here, and my emotions have been running high all day.

Kwame: I'm surely glad that Louise led such an effective session this afternoon to help us see our built-in racism and the subtle ways in which we really don't support our leaders of color.

George: We made good progress on our financial situation. We have decided on the first steps to turn our problems around in that area.

Angela: I'm glad we were able to address both the issues of support for our leaders of color and our financial situation. I don't think that would have happened if Teresa had not been so effective using the reflection process.

Samuel: I would surely love to learn to use the E-I-A-G disciplined reflection in a meeting. Teresa stepped right in and saved the day.

Teresa: [to Samuel] No time like the present. Why don't I coach you on facilitating an I-A-G right here in this meeting?

Samuel: [to Teresa and the team] I'd love to have you do that. Is that OK with the rest of you?

The other three members of the team nodded their heads in agreement.

Teresa: We've only been meeting for a few minutes, but I will bet you there is already plenty of interesting data that is not fully visible to us as a team.

Teresa: [to Samuel] Why don't you use the chart paper to list some of the possible statements or actions as a focus for our learning?

Samuel: [to Teresa] You mean you want me to record the I-A-G on the chart paper?

Teresa: [to Samuel] Yes, that way there is a visual record of the I-A-G. It is particularly useful when you are first facilitating the I-A-G disciplined reflection, or when the group is unfamiliar with the reflection process. Do you know what to do first?

Samuel: [to Teresa] You have indicated that we are using our meeting time right here as our Experience. Now I need to solicit a focus for the I-A-G. I'm into the Identification step.

Teresa nodded in agreement.

Samuel: [to the team] What has happened in the past few minutes we have been together from which we might learn?

Teresa: [to Samuel] You might want to expand that just a bit to focus on both the curiosity for learning and where any emotions were elicited.

Samuel: [to Teresa and the team] OK. Did anything happen that raised an emotional reaction for you and from which you would like to learn?

Angela: I was curious about all the emotions that Samuel said were present with him.

Samuel records this identified focus on the chart paper.

Samuel: Any others?

George: I wondered how Teresa responded to Angela's praise in terms of the way she used the I-A-G.

Samuel records this identified focus on the chart paper.

| *Identify*

Kwame: I had a twitch in my stomach when George changed the subject and talked about our financial situation.

Teresa: [to Samuel] As you list that third possible identified moment, note that there is more information in each of these than a simple focus. However, you can now see which one the group wants to choose and then clarify the focus.

Samuel: [to the team] Let's have a show of hands to indicate which of these three you would like to use as the focus for our I-A-G.

All three of the hands went up for Kwame's statement about George changing the subject.

Samuel: [to Teresa] How do I clarify this focus? It seems that Kwame is reporting an emotional reaction to George's statement and making an assumption about George's intentions.

Teresa: [to Samuel] Just go back to George's statement. Kwame's feelings and attributions will be a part of the later steps in the I-A-G. Everyone is ready to work with that specific statement of George's.

Samuel: [to the team] My memory is that George said that he thought we made good progress in connection with our financial situation.

Angela: I heard him add that we had decided upon the first steps on how to turn the financial situation around.

Samuel: I remember that, too. Are we all agreed on what George said?

Everyone nodded.

Analyze | **Samuel:** Now I'm ready to solicit the thoughts, feelings and actions in response to what George said.

Teresa: [to Samuel] Not quite yet. You haven't checked with George to see if he is OK with having the focus on him and his statement.

Samuel: [to Teresa and then to George] I almost forgot that. George, is it OK if we I-A-G your statement that you thought we made good progress in connection with our financial situation and that we had made the decision on the first steps we need to take to turn the finances around?

George: That's fine with me. I'm not sure why there is so much interest in my statement, but I bet I'll have something to learn from the reflection process.

Samuel: Let's start by finding out what thoughts you had when George made his statement about the good progress we've made in connection with our financial situation and that we had decided which steps to take in order to turn the finances around. [to Teresa] Should I continue to record on the chart paper?

Teresa: [to Samuel] Yes, you might make lists for thoughts, feelings and actions. And don't forget to remind George to listen only while he hears others' responses first.

Samuel: [to George] So your job, George, is to remain silent and listen while the others tell us their reactions to your statement. Then you'll have a chance to share your reaction.

George: OK, I'm all ears. And I hope I have an open mind.

Samuel makes the headings on the chart paper.

Samuel: [to team] Your thoughts?

Kwame: I thought George changed the subject, and I thought he was discounting my statement as a black male about the important work toward racial understanding that we had in the afternoon.

Angela: As a Latina I can understand Kwame's reaction.

Samuel: [to Angela] And what were your thoughts at the time George made his statement?

Teresa: [to Samuel] That's great, Samuel; keep the focus on the reactions at the time of the incident – in this case, when George made his statement.

Angela: Well, I was taking in the importance of Kwame's statement when George spoke, and I shifted and listened to George and found that I agreed with him.

Samuel: [to Angela] And your feelings?

Angela: My feelings of satisfaction about what happened today were reinforced by George's statement. I think there was some joy in my heart since we really did good work today. But it seems that you, Kwame, felt differently.

Samuel: [to Teresa] Is it OK to let Angela lead the process along?

Teresa: [to Samuel] You bet. Your job is to facilitate the process, not to control it. When groups get really good at using the I-A-G, they don't need any designated person as facilitator.

Samuel: [to Kwame] How did you feel?

Kwame: That twitch in my stomach was anger. I was feeling discounted.

Samuel: Any other thoughts or feelings? (Pause) Did any of you do anything in reaction to George's statement?

Angela: I followed with a statement acknowledging the importance of what both Kwame and George said and credited Louise with her effective use of the I-A-G disciplined reflection.

Kwame: And I looked over at George to try to see if he as a white male had any idea how I reacted to his statement.

Teresa: [to Samuel] Now you have recorded the first part of the Analysis on the chart paper. I suspect you have uncovered most of the relevant data. I suggest you move to checking assumptions.

Samuel: [to Teresa] I don't exactly know what to say.

Teresa: [to Samuel] You can just ask a direct question like this: Did you make any assumptions about others at the time of the incident?

Samuel: I'll just practice asking the question. Given what you have heard, did you make any assumptions about others?

Angela: I don't think I made any assumptions other than taking what was said by both George and Kwame at face value.

Kwame: I am clearly making assumptions about George. I need to hear from him. I'm concerned that as a white male he may not have learned anything from this afternoon's work with Louise.

Samuel: We'll hear from George in a moment. Based on the data we now have, what was the effect of George's statement on the group?

Angela: I think that George's statement created thoughts and feelings that could have festered if we hadn't gone through the I-A-G process. I want to hear from George.

Samuel: [to George] You've been patient and listening. Can you tell us your intentions when you made the statement?

George: I really am glad that I just listened. It gave me a chance to let go of some of my defensiveness. I assure you my original intentions were not to put you down, Kwame. I was just focused on the success we made in addressing the financial situation. I was totally unaware of your reaction to me, Kwame. I was making the assumption that everyone saw the meeting as I did and that the progress on the financial front was just as critical as the racial understanding.

Kwame: And I was assuming that you were discounting me.

Angela: It sounds as if you both were acting out your assumptions based on your racial identity groups. And I'll bet you have some learnings that I would like to hear.

Generalize |

Teresa: [to Samuel] By this time, if folks are functioning with open minds, the assumptions will be acknowledged and the learnings will often be obvious as in this case. It is a good idea to return to the chart paper and capture the learnings even if they are obvious since publicly stating them will help reinforce any change of behavior.

Samuel: OK, it is time for learnings. Let's start with you, George.

George: Obviously, as a white male, I need to be more sensitive to the reaction I create in others.

Samuel: What specifically would that mean you would do in another situation like this?

George: One thing that might have helped this time was to acknowledge Kwame's statement so he knows I have really heard him before I make my statement. Active listening is always important, but it is particularly important when I am listening to a person of color. It is so easy for me to fall into the trap of assuming everyone sees the world the way I do. I've been totally conditioned that way.

Samuel: Anything else?

George: Although no one said anything about it this time, I know that I tend to come on as though my opinion is the truth. I am continually learning that a servant-leader is one who is self-aware and understands his effect on others. This reflection has really helped me once again to stay true to my journey as a servant-leader.

Samuel: How about the others? Learnings?

Kwame: Once again I learned how my internal rage over racism in the society gets reflected in anger over things before I check them out.

Samuel: What would you do in the future?

Kwame: It's so obvious. As soon as I felt the twitch in my stomach, I could have stopped and checked the assumptions I was making. I believe checking it out with the other person immediately would work for me when I am on a team like this.

Samuel: Angela, any learnings?

Angela: You bet. Now I am absolutely committed to the I-A-G reflection process. I saw Teresa use it effectively with the annual meeting today; now I've seen you do it effectively with our team. I want to be the next one to be coached in using the I-A-G.

Teresa: [to Samuel and the team] You did a terrific job, Samuel. I'm certainly glad that as servant-leaders we are committed to using the E-I-A-G disciplined reflection. It truly is a satisfying experience.

TIPS FOR FACILITATING | AN E-I-A-G

Participating in disciplined reflection is important for the servant-leader to become more aware at all levels: intrapersonal, interpersonal, group and organization. However, the skill of actually leading or facilitating disciplined reflection in a group setting is also an important part of becoming a servant-leader. Following are some **guidelines for the facilitation of the E-I-A-G disciplined reflection.**

Tips for the **experience** stage:
• The experience for the disciplined reflection can be the most recent meeting or session of a group. Or it can be the point at which an incident occurs and from which valuable learning can take place.
• Some groups set aside reflection time at the end of each session. This might be a norm for the group; it can also be an intentional part of the agenda.
• Reflection time is also important at a time of high emotion or tension or when the group is blocked; this might be a time of confusion or conflict. Action can be stopped for the disciplined reflection.

Tips for the **identify** stage:
• The identification step is the first part of the reflection process. Most important is making sure the identified incident from the experience is clear.
• It is important that the identified incident be specific. The more specific it is, the more likely the reflection process will lead to rich learnings. Be as specific as possible: Use a comment someone makes or a specific action that occurs.
• When first facilitating an I-A-G with a group, use chart paper in front of the room to provide a visual record of the steps in the I-A-G.
• Solicit several incidents as possibilities for the focus of the I-A-G. These can be listed on the chart paper.

- Determine which incident will be the single focus for the I-A-G. This might be done by a show of hands for each of the incidents to identify the group's energy.
- Check with the person on whom the I-A-G is focused to secure permission to proceed. Be sure that this person only listens until the others have shared their reactions.

Tips for the **analyze** stage:
- The first part of the analysis is soliciting the thoughts, feelings and actions of others in response to the incident.
- Start by soliciting the thoughts at the time of the identified incident. It usually is easier to solicit thoughts than feelings. Additional probing for the feelings may be necessary since many people are less able to articulate their feelings.
- Using chart paper in front of the room helps in this analysis. Use separate lists for thoughts, feelings and actions to clarify the responses. This also helps groups identify the difference between a thought and a feeling.
- Check assumptions individuals may have had about others at the time of the incident. Some of these assumptions may have changed based on data in the reflection process. It is useful for all of this data to be shared.
- Continue the analysis by determining the effect of the incident on the group.
- Finally, turn to the identified person and ask her for her intentions as well as her thoughts, feelings and actions.
- After the intention of the identified person is known, others may want to revise their original assumptions.

Before drawing learnings from the reflection process, an additional connection can be made to the spiritual level or the beliefs of a faith community. Questions such as *Were you aware of an intangible force, energy, power, or spirit as we went through our reflection process? What more can you say regarding that?* Or alternatively, *Does this incident remind you of any episode in your faith heritage — whether from your oral tradition or in your sacred text such as the Koran, Torah or Bible?* This connection with the spiritual level or perspectives of a faith community then becomes a part of the reflection in order to enhance the learning.

Tips for the **generalize** stage:

• The identified person states his learnings first. This often includes a statement of what the person would do in a similar situation in the future.

• The others then state their learnings and applications to future situations. Since each learning is unique to an individual, learnings may seem contradictory.

But, first, what is power? Secondly, where does it come from?

Victor Hugo

Les Misérables

To live in a quantum world, to weave here and there with ease and grace, we will need to change what we do. We will need to stop describing tasks and instead facilitate process. We will need to become savvy about how to build relationships, how to nurture growing, evolving things. All of us need better skills in listening, communicating, and facilitating groups, because these are the talents that build strong relationships. ... The quantum world has demolished the concept of the unconnected individual.

Margaret J. Wheatley

Leadership and The New Science

Shared power makes groups strong, healthy and productive.

Katherine Elberfeld, Founder

Gabriel Center for Servant-Leadership

Man's natural mindset is to wish to dominate.

Napoleon Bonaparte

In the long run, no leader is privileged to 'lord it over' anyone, in any system, because the universe itself is constructed to honor the freedom of the human spirit. Systems that violate such freedom are doomed to topple in the revolt of subjugated children, oppressed employees, and tyrannized citizens, however long it takes. This is why servant leadership is foundational. Like a rock on which to anchor a house, it will secure any structure of human enterprise built upon it – families, businesses, churches, nations – as well as the emerging network of nations in their interlocking need of one another for the peace and protection of the planet.

Bennett J. Sims

Servanthood: Leadership for the Third Millenium

Peace is not won by those who fiercely guard their differences but by those who with open minds and hearts seek out connections.

Katherine Paterson

Words of Women, Quotations for Success

Let us, with John Lennon, imagine.

When we operate in formal organizations, we negotiate chaos and "permanent whitewater." In this section, we will examine chaos and change agents, managing polarities, and using disciplined reflection in organizations. We will also look at examples of individuals and organizations that uphold servant-leader values. An exercise in casting values, vision, and mission helps us maintain those values at the organizational level.

characteristics of servant-leader organizations

In many ways, the idea that an organization can be a servant is a strange concept. Our beliefs and experience tell us that only people can serve, that organizations have no flesh or sinew or heart. Renowned author Margaret Wheatley helps us understand that organizations are composed of dynamic, evolving human beings and we cannot ignore the deep realities of human existence when trying to understand the systems in which we are involved. Wheatley bases much of her work on a servant-leader approach to systems. She believes that Robert Greenleaf was well attuned to the clash between the forces of domination in corporate cultures and the forces of life and freedom within people.

More than thirty years of experience have proven that large and small organizations can operate with a true servant-leader philosophy. It's not easy. It is not a "quick fix" or "management flavor of the month" approach. A servant-led organization requires a foundation of values, trust and open communication. While time and dedication are required, the long-term benefits can be transformative for both the employees and the organization.

Organizations do not change to a servant-leadership culture overnight. In most cases, it takes years, but any honest effort shows immediate results. As leaders of these organizations describe their ongoing journeys, they include common themes.

change: Crisis may force organizations to look at the way they function. Employee dissatisfaction, poor quality or a simple realization that work is missing the spirit of life can trigger change.

champions: Champions can come from any level of the organization. They should be trusted by others. It helps if some champions are at least at the middle management level or higher.

conversations: Questions are raised with staff and board: Who are we? Who do we want to be? How can we be an organization of distinction? What stands in the way? How can we learn to trust each other?

mission: Claim the mission. Clear, succinct vision and mission statements are drafted, redrafted and drafted again until all agree with them. These are not abstract, purely conceptual proclamations, but expressions of the real aspirations of all employees.

vision: In the process of drafting vision and mission statements, a new metaphor of the institution usually bubbles up. It is often related to the words "community," "organic," "partnerships" or "service."

accountability: Servant-leadership is not "soft." It demands new kinds of responsibilities and accountabilities.

evolution: Without exception, servant-led organizations are open to reexamination of their most basic assumptions. They know today's organizations must thrive in today's organizational climate, which author Peter Vaill describes as "permanent whitewater."

change agents and chaos

There was a time when the future was more predictable. Goals could be set and action plans developed to achieve those goals. However, the pace of today's society is different. Conditions change. There is more variability. Often our orderly structured organizations are not able to keep up with fast-paced change. Two contrasting metaphors for managing and planning for change are a peaceful lake and permanent whitewater.

A canoe being paddled across a peaceful lake toward a destination on the other side is a metaphor for the rational, orderly manner in which change can be managed when all the elements are predictable. You know how to get to the other side. A kayak in whitewater, however, must navigate the forces of the river as they arrive. There is no time to focus on the pine tree ahead and go

Flatwater and Whitewater

straight there. In fact, it is dangerous to do so. Timely responses must be made that allow us to avoid the next rock and to find the course that will allow us to continue on the journey without crashing into more rocks or spinning out of control. Certainly this is a much closer metaphor to the realities of our rapidly changing world.

The servant-leader's ability to be a change agent in an organization is essential. He or she must first envision images that will enable the organization to navigate the permanent whitewater. This is where the development of the ideas about chaos in the physical sciences provides new mental models for the servant-leader. The reality of chaos is that it is self-organizing under a wide range of conditions of certainty and uncertainty. When there is a lot of certainty and a lot of agreement the elements are orderly, predictable and organized. Rational, linear decision-making can be applied here. This is the kind of change that can be managed by keeping the metaphor of the canoe on a peaceful lake in mind.

As the certainty diminishes and there is less agreement on a course of action, however, the metaphor of permanent whitewater fits better. If there is very little certainty and there are so many alternatives there is no agreement, the future is unpredictable and random. This is like approaching a twenty-foot waterfall rather than navigable whitewater. This is chaos out of control.

In between the tightly organized and the totally unorganized system there is much space for self-organizing in which the system or organization is adapting and emerging and where learning is taking place. This is when the metaphor of permanent whitewater is important to hold in mind in order to navigate effectively. This is where the chaos is productively self-organizing.

The language of complex adaptive systems is used to describe this self-organizing space. Complex adaptive systems are complex in that they are made up of a variety of diverse elements that are connected to each other and are adaptive because they can change, learn and grow as circumstances and experience require. Complex adaptive systems evolve according to three principles:

- Order is emergent as opposed to hierarchical — for example, in self-organizing space there is sufficient information for new patterns of communication or order that could not be determined in advance by a leader.

- The system's history is irreversible — whatever has happened in the past exists in the system.
- The system's future is unpredictable.

The people and groups in the system are semi-autonomous and seek to maximize some measure of goodness by evolving over time. Driven by these principles, self-directed work teams — whether small or large groups — function effectively in such settings.

Many servant-leader organizations have created more self-organizing space in changing the way things are done. Herb Kelleher, co-founder of Southwest Airlines, says, "If you create an environment where people truly participate you don't need to control. They know what needs to be done and they do it."

The figure "Order Out of Chaos," which was developed by organization development and workforce diversity consultant Ed Olson, illustrates what happens when the servant-leader change agent, or others, changes the interactions in a system. Some chaos is introduced into the system, and that allows a new pattern to emerge. The servant-leader change agent must be willing to trust that order will emerge from chaos just as boiling water begins to roll in a systematic way after the chaos at the beginning of the boiling. Traditionally many leaders, for numerous reasons, have not been willing to let go of the control of the system or trust that self-organizing can or will occur.

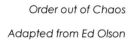

Order out of Chaos

Adapted from Ed Olson

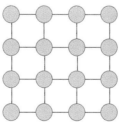 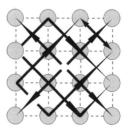 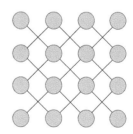

initial **interactions**   **chaos** in the system   resulting **pattern**

The following figure, which was developed by Ed Olson and Glenda Eoyang, is particularly useful to the servant-leader change agents in their ability to create complex adaptive systems. There are three basic elements or conditions for self-organizing: 1) the container, 2) the significant differences and 3) the transforming exchanges. This is different from the mental model for organizations or systems usually held by leaders. The servant-leader can focus attention on these three conditions for self-organizing and allow the self-organizing to take place effectively. The container is made up of such elements as meetings, mission statements, budget, procedures and norms. The significant differences are the people with different knowledge, skills and expectations, as well as the diversity represented by different social identity groups. And the transforming exchanges are the dialogues, discussions and conversations that lead to new patterns.

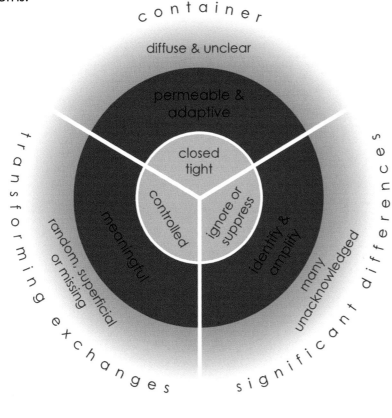

Conditions of Self-Organizing
by Ed Olson and Glenda Eoyang

As the figure above illustrates, if the container is closed and tight, significant differences are suppressed or ignored and/or the transforming exchanges are controlled, self-organizing will not take place. However, if the container is too open or porous, and the significant differences are not acknowledged, or there are too many, and/or the transforming exchanges are random, superficial or missing, the chaos will be out of control. The conditions for self-organizing are best met when the container is permeable and adaptive, when the significant differences are identified and amplified and when the transforming exchanges are meaningful contacts. As a change agent, the servant-leader can be aware of these three conditions and influence and make adjustments.

The three conditions of self-organizing are represented by aspects of bread-making in this metaphor for a complex adaptive system. The bowl is the container; the ingredients represent the significant differences; and the yeast is the catalyst for change in the form of transforming exchanges. The role of the servant-leader change agent as bread-maker is to make sure the container is appropriate, the rich varied ingredients represent the significant differences that will create a bread of value, and being sure the yeast is present so the transforming exchanges take place. Like the bread-maker, the servant-leader change agent kneads the ingredients in the bread from time to time and has the patience to allow the yeast to do its work by letting the bread rise. Finally, the finished product is a delicious loaf of bread.

There are a number of different settings in which the following exercise can be used to understand the concept of self-organizing in a complex adaptive system. It can be used by a facilitator in a training session for servant-leaders when they are learning about the concept of self-organizing. Consultants and leaders can use the exercise to help an organization understand the dynamics that exist within the system or organization. Frequently when the exercise is used in a system or organization, the dynamics that occur become a metaphor for the self-organizing systems in the organization. Reflection on the exercise by the leader can provide insights about what changes need to be made in the container, the significant differences and/or the transforming interactions that will or can unleash the creativity of the complex adaptive system.

Self-Organizing Exercise ✋

The exercise is effective for numbers in a group as small as 10 and as large as 100. The space must be large enough to allow the free circulation of the people who are engaged in the exercise. The participants are told the following:

Stand in the room at least an arm's length from any other person.

Keep your eyes closed. (You can use blindfolds if you wish.)

Choose a number from one to 100. Do not share the number until told to do so.

Form a circle with the numbers in ascending order, but speak to only one person at a time and only when you are touching that person.

Pay attention to your thoughts and feelings.

During the exercise, the facilitator/consultant/leader does not in any way interfere with what happens. Whatever happens are data for the reflection. The exercise continues until the group has finished.

Once the participants believe they have completed the task, have them open their eyes and locate the person who chose the smallest number. Then ask the individuals in the group to announce their numbers in order around the circle. Thoughts and feelings can then be solicited. If critical incidents have occurred, the disciplined reflection process of E-I-A-G might be used to identify learnings. During the reflection, the focus can be on the three elements: the container, significant differences and transforming interchanges.

Questions can be asked to identify what allowed the group to effectively, or not effectively, self-organize and how these three elements could be altered to self-organize as a complex adaptive system.

In this exercise the container, the significant differences and the transforming interactions are simplified for the purposes of easy identification. The container is initially set by the venue, the directions and the rules. The significant differences are provided through the exercise by choosing different numbers. Of course all the inherent diversity of the participants also becomes a part of the significant differences. The transforming interactions are initially structured by the rule to speak to only one person at a time and only when you are touching that person. Of course once the exercise starts there are ample opportunities for transformative interactions that will enable the group to finish the task.

CASE STUDY IN COMPLEX | ADAPTIVE SYSTEMS

IMPACT Silver Spring, a small nonprofit organization in Silver Spring, Maryland, used the principles of a complex adaptive system to organize an open space diversity conference in the community. The conference itself was a self-organizing open space event in which more than 300 people declared their passions and convened groups around their particular interests. Conversations were held that had never happened in the community. There was just enough structure in the event for transformational exchanges to take place. This resulting conference was like the delicious loaf of bread in the bread-making metaphor. Nothing like a diversity conference had been experienced in this community of changing demographics in the suburbs of Washington, D.C. From the beginning, the volunteer who saw the value of such a conference organized it using the principles of complex adaptive systems. There was no money for such a conference. The coordinating committee for the conference started with a couple of people gathering in one of their homes. People then invited others who seemed to provide different perspectives or resources to the meetings. There was no fixed group doing the planning. Whoever came were the right people. However, a virtual coordinating committee of more than sixty people developed through an e-mail list over a period of months. The involvement and the commitment of the people were such that when the original organizer who was to facilitate the actual open space event was too ill to participate, the conference unfolded in all its splendor as new leadership evolved. Focusing on the container, the significant differences and the transformational exchanges was a highly productive way to accomplish this volunteer event.

Margaret Wheatley cogently sums up the power of allowing self-organizing principles to work in our organizations when she writes in *Leadership and the New Science*:

> Information is unique as a resource because of its capacity to generate itself. It's the solar energy of organization – inexhaustible with new progeny emerging every time information meets up with itself. As long as there are senders and receivers linked together in a context, fertility abounds. All that is needed is freedom of circulation to guarantee new births. In fact, the greatest generator of information is chaos, where so much spawning of information goes on that researchers feel obliged to monitor every moment of

the system's activity lest they miss something.

Of course, this is exactly what we fear. We have no desire to let information roam about, to let it procreate promiscuously where it will, to create chaos. Our management task is to enforce control, to keep information contained, to pass it down in such a way that no procreation occurs. Information chastity belts are a central management function. The last thing we need is information running loose in our organizations ... but if information is to function as a self-generating source of organizational vitality, we must abandon our dark cloaks of control and trust in the principles of self-organization, even in our own organizations.

managing polarities

Leaders and organizations that manage polarities well outperform those that don't.
Barry Johnson

People in our society often think in dichotomies. We are brought up on "either/or" thinking. Eastern philosophy is based more on holding what seem like two opposites as interdependent pairs. Organization Development consultant Barry Johnson has developed ways to understand and manage these interdependent pairs. He calls them polarities. Polarities are not problems to be solved; they can only be managed. Servant-leaders who are prepared to manage polarities in organizations will be more effective because they will not waste their time trying to resolve difficulties that are not really problems to be solved.

Many polarities in organizations do not respond to the usual problem-solving steps: Stability/Change, Individual/Team, Autocratic/Participatory, Centralized/Decentralized and many others. For all these polarities the answer to each of the following two questions is a "Yes."

> • *Is the difficulty ongoing?* Yes, if it is a polarity. Problems are not necessarily ongoing. Problems have a solution that can be considered an end point in the process.

> • *Are there two poles that are interdependent?* Yes, if it is a polarity. The solution to problems can stand alone. The two poles are independent.

Once you recognize a polarity with its two poles, it is important to think about the underlying energy system in all polarities that takes the form of an infinity loop. Barry Johnson describes this energy system with the simple example of breathing — exhaling and inhaling. There is a natural oscillation of energy around these two poles that takes the shape of an infinity loop. The following explanation and breathing diagrams are from his book, *Managing Polarities in Congregations: Eight Keys for Thriving Faith Communities*. This example is very simple, but it does demonstrate the natural oscillation between two poles that is central to all polarities.

Focus on your own breathing for a moment. Exhale deeply and hold it. As you hold it, you start to experience the limits of exhaling alone which is (A), a lack of oxygen. Now inhale deeply and hold it. Notice how natural and good it feels to move from the downside of exhaling (A) to the upside of inhaling (B) as you get fresh oxygen. However, as we see in the following, this move to the upside of inhaling is not a sustainable "solution" to the breathing issue.

| **INFINITY LOOP**

Breathing Cycles

by Barry Johnson

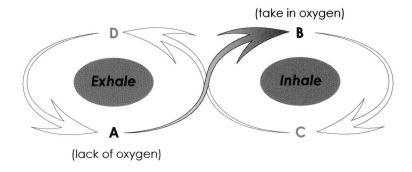

After getting the benefits of inhaling, you start to experience the limits of inhaling alone, which is (C), excess carbon dioxide. Again you experience discomfort — go ahead and exhale. Notice how good it feels to move from the downside of inhaling (C) to the upside of exhaling (D) as you clean out the carbon dioxide.

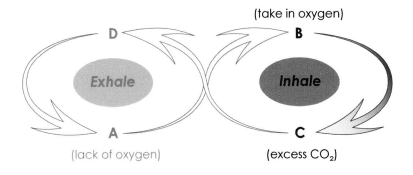

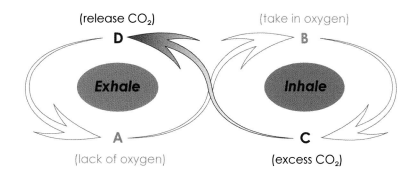

Cleaning out carbon dioxide is the wonderful benefit of exhaling. It is essential and it is also not a "solution" to the breathing issue. After getting the benefits of exhaling, you start to experience the limits of exhaling alone which is a lack of oxygen (A). The energy continues to follow this infinity loop as long as you live. Below is a summary of the self-correcting oscillation within the breathing polarity:

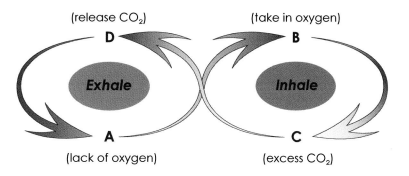

**POLARITY |
MANAGEMENT**

The Polarity Management worksheet provides a useful way to explore the ups and downs of a polarity. The two poles can be indicated in the boxes on the left and the right sides of the worksheet. On the left side of the worksheet the positive results from focusing on this pole

Polarity Management

Worksheet

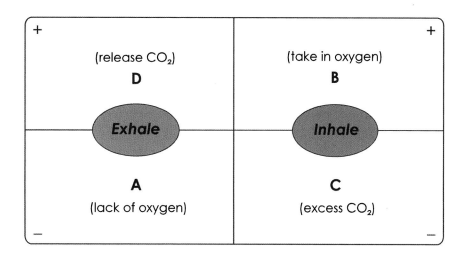

are listed in the upper left quadrant. The negative results from over-focusing on the left pole to the neglect of the right side are listed in the lower left quadrant. Likewise, the positive results from focusing on the right pole are listed in the upper right quadrant while the negative results from over-focusing on the right pole to the neglect of the left side are listed in the lower right quadrant.

Let's consider the Stability/Change polarity that is always one of the challenges of the servant-leader. This is definitely a polarity. The difficulty of figuring out how to address the issues of stability and change in an organization or system is ongoing. The two poles are interdependent because too much stability affects change, and too much change affects stability. It is clear that there is an upside to stability, and there is an upside to change. And it is also clear that there is a downside to stability and a downside to change.

Now we can use the Polarity Management worksheet to examine the Stability/Change polarity. Display the polarity by writing "Stability" on one side of the horizontal axis and writing "Change" on the other side. Then think of what comes to mind when you think of the positives associated with stability and write those words in the quadrant above the word "Stability." Do the same for the "Change" side. Next reflect on what words come to mind when thinking of the negatives of each side of the polarity and write those words in the quadrants below. Now you have a Polarity Management worksheet that looks something like the following:

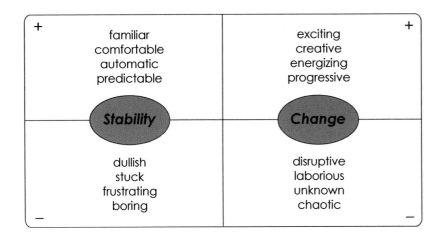

The Stability & Change Polarity

Now if we superimpose the underlying energy field for this Stability/Change polarity we can begin to see how to manage this polarity effectively as servant-leaders. In any organization there will be a rhythm for this energy field. In fact, there may be an interruption of a healthy flow of energy. At a point in time the organization may be stuck in one of the negative quadrants. Conscious understanding of what is happening will enable the servant-leader to help the organization manage the polarity effectively. The task of the organization or system is to maximize the positive quadrants while still recognizing the negative quadrants. This is demonstrated by having the infinity loop go high into the upside of each pole and not go very low into the downside of either pole.

For instance, it is important for those in the organization who want change to understand that those who want stability are looking at the downside of change, not the positive aspects of change. The optimal infinity loop in the following diagram recognizes that the downsides will be experienced, but the emphasis is on the positive sides of both stability and change. If there are those in the organization who are champions of change, it is likely that they are feeling the downside of stability. The harder they push for change the more those comfortable with stability will focus on the downside of change. The servant-leader manager can facilitate the flow through this infinity loop by encouraging those who are pushing for change to take the time to listen actively to the concerns of those

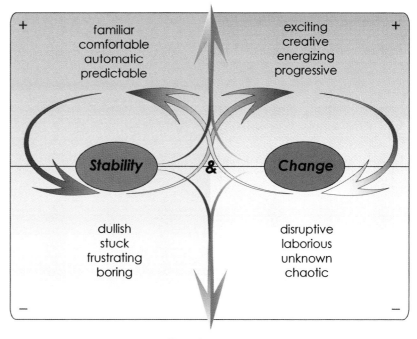

Managing the Stability & Change Polarity

focusing on the downside of change, making it easier for them to let go of their fears. The servant-leader manager needs to be alert always to the totality of the dynamics.

In addition to the infinity loop, several other additions have been made to make this a more complete picture of the Stability/Change polarity. Right in the middle the "&" has been added to emphasize that both poles are important. Also the "Effective Servant-Leader" label has been added at the top to remind us of our ultimate purpose. John Scherer suggested calling this the Greater Purpose Statement. The synergy of emphasizing the positive aspects of both "Stability" and "Change" is represented by the intertwining arrows leading to an effective servant-leader. The intertwining arrows on the bottom of the diagram indicate the negative synergy of emphasizing the downside of "Stability" and "Change." This area can represent our deepest fears. The following generalized polarity diagram is a useful tool in the hands of the effective servant-leader:

Greater Purpose Statement

+

positive results
from focusing on
left pole

positive results
from focusing on
right pole

+

Left Pole

&

Right Pole

negative results
from over focusing on
right pole to the
neglect of the left pole

negative results
from over focusing on
left pole to the
neglect of the right pole

−

−

Achieving the

Greater Purpose

Deeper Fear

The following exercise is a good way to learn both the concept of managing polarities and actually to work with polarities in the system or organization. The purpose of the exercise is to engage the participants in physically experiencing moving from one position to another in the four quadrants of the polarity management worksheet following the two upper loops and the two lower loops of the infinity loop. Often the insights gained enable the organization to move to new levels of understanding and action.

Stability & Change
Polarity Exercise

The exercise involves both identifying the positive and negative aspects of both poles and experiencing the energy system by moving along the infinity loop. Depending on the needs of the group or organization the emphasis can be placed differently on each of these.

The exercise is most effective for groups from 8 to 32. For groups larger than 32 it is useful to set up multiple groups each doing the exercise in a parallel fashion in the same room.

Replicate the Polarity Management worksheet by dividing the space in the room into the four quadrants. It is often useful to use masking tape on the floor with the two poles being represented by labels on pieces of paper on the floor. Place a flip chart in each of the four quadrants. Enough room needs to be provided for subgroups from two to eight people to move among the four quadrants. If the primary emphasis is to be placed on experiencing the energy in the infinity loop, the masking tape can be used simply to form the infinity loop around the two poles represented by two pieces of paper on the floor.

The participants may have a polarity to explore that is key to the organization's development. If they are uncertain which polarity to choose, it is often useful to examine the Stability/Change polarity and the way it is managed. For illustrative purposes below, the directions will be given as if the Stability/Change polarity had been chosen. The facilitator tells the participants the following:

We will be working this Stability/Change polarity. The polarity worksheet has been replicated on the floor. (The facilitator points to the positive quadrant of stability, the negative quadrant of stability, the positive quadrant of change and the negative quadrant of change.)

You will be divided into four groups to move on the infinity loop through the four quadrants of the polarity. Count off by fours with the number ones going to the negative quadrant of stability, the number twos going to the positive quadrant of change, the number threes going to the negative quadrant of change and the number fours going to the positive quadrant of stability.

In your quadrant write on the flip chart all the words that come to mind when you think about that quadrant.

After a minute or two depending on the size of the subgroups, tell them to stop their writing.

You will now move to the next quadrant in the infinity loop discussed above and add any new words for that quadrant on the flip chart. The subgroup in the negative quadrant for stability will move to the positive quadrant of change; the subgroup in the positive quadrant of change will move to the negative quadrant of change; the subgroup in the negative quadrant of change will move to the positive quadrant for stability; the subgroup in the positive quadrant of stability will move to the negative quadrant of stability.

(This previous step is repeated until all groups have visited each quadrant.) Now that you are in the last of the four quadrants following the infinity loop, your task is to take the words listed and draw a picture with no words summarizing the list created by the previous groups.

After each group has reported the picture for its quadrant, the reflection can begin. The reflection can focus on the reactions of subgroups in different quadrants as well as the dynamic of moving from one quadrant to another on the infinity loop. Connections with the organization or system will be clearer.

servant-leaders in the system

Steven Covey claims the leaders of the future are the same as the leaders of our present. There will be no change in personnel. The changes will be an internal "inside-out" transformation.

Jim Collins' book *Good to Great* illustrates how he and his research team identified a set of eleven companies that achieved great results and sustained those results for fifteen years. The companies generated stock returns that beat the general stock market by an average of seven times in fifteen years, better than twice the results delivered by a composite index of some of the world's greatest companies such as Coca-Cola, General Electric and Merck. The servant-leader approach of the CEOs was a critical factor in the organizations' success. Collins and the team discussed using the term "servant-leadership" but chose the term **Level 5** to be more encompassing of the traits they wished to portray.

Leadership exemplified by the top executives was a critical factor in the companies' success. All of the executives, according to Collins' *Good to Great*, exhibited the following servant-leader or Level 5 traits when they would:

- embody a paradoxical mix of personal humility and professional will;
- display a compelling modesty, are self-effacing and understated;
- exhibit a workmanlike diligence — more plow horse than show horse;
- set up their successors for even greater success in the next generation;

- produce sustained results; and
- take full responsibility for failures, do not assign blame to others for disappointing results.

According to George SanFacon, University of Michigan, formal leaders fall somewhere on a continuum of possibilities between the extremes of boss and servant-leader. The boss uses power in a command and control manner, while the servant-leader models service and moral responsibility as outlined below:

bosses   **servant-leaders**

governance

take an authoritarian approach   take a participatory approach
hold unilateral power   share power & vulnerability

accountability & control

hold accountability with control   hold accountability without control

periodically judge the   are firsts among equals
performance of each employee

control when, how and if   gives & recieves honest
performance reviews happen   feedback

goals

maintain existing authority &   practice moral symmetry
privilege

strive to meet the needs of   strive to balance legitimate
particular stakeholders   needs of everyone

focus

take care of what already is   evoke & shape what is possible

view of others

view subordinates as a   view colleagues as partners &
means to an end   ends in themselves

meaning of work

view work as a transaction   view work as a co-creative act
whereby time and energy are   of individuality and community
exchanged for money

The Spectrum of Leadership

Adapted from George SanFacon

Consideration of others. Openness to discussion. Care for the needs of other people rather than control and power over them. Compassion. Thoughtfulness. Integrity. Authenticity. Qualities all of servant-leaders. And yet, because we are human beings, because living and working according to the servant-leader model takes a lifetime to learn, is a lifelong journey, we walk along the path and sometimes stumble on rocky ground or get caught in thorny vines.

We as human beings are flawed; we struggle. Sometimes we achieve more closely the goal of living out the values of servant-leadership; sometimes, we have opportunities to learn from difficult or disappointing experiences. Spiritual writer Anne Lamott puts it well in her book *Plan B* when she says,

> Your problem is how you are going to spend this one odd and precious life you have been issued. Whether you're going to live it trying to look good and creating the illusion that you have power over people and circumstances, or whether you are going to taste it, enjoy it, and find out the truth about who you are.

But we do struggle; we do keep trying to go forward on the path. And that is where the power is: the fact that we keep on trying in the midst of our flaws, in the midst of our frailties, in the midst of our confusion. The fact that it is a struggle makes it all the more powerful than if the path were smooth with no rocks, no stumbling, no thorny vines to ensnare.

In this section, we have a collection of stories about people who have in a large part of their lives exemplified the servant-leader model. Each has demonstrated servant-leader qualities – compassion, thoughtfulness, integrity, authenticity.

And yet, with each one, you or we can name flaws, times when the person's life and the model of servant-leadership did not match up in a way that we would have liked to see, times when his or her behavior disappointed or confused us.

And that is the heart of their stories, that is where we find the power: the impulse to serve others in the midst of challenges that come both from within and from without.

So, it is not perfect human beings we present to you in this section. It is humanity at its best — flawed, but trying. Frail but moving forward along the path.

Moving from oppression to freedom. Extending social justice to all. Reaching out to the forgotten, the voiceless, the overlooked. All at the heart of being a servant-leader. And all held dear in the hearts of four women, separated from each other and from us by time, land and the waters.

Queen Ka'ahumanu of Hawaii; Wilma Mankiller, former principal chief of the Cherokee Nation of Oklahoma; Mother Teresa of India and Diana, Princess of Wales.

These four women, all leaders of their country or in their community, shook up the ways of their people and led them to a place of health and freedom unknown to them before. And all four women show us what it means to serve the people entrusted to our care even as we lead them.

The massive Queen Ka'ahumanu at six feet tall became the first *kuhina nui*, or premier, of Hawaii, sharing leadership with the king. She focused much of her work on eliminating the taboos under which women suffered in the traditional religion of the islands, and she developed Hawaii's first codified laws, based on Christian values.

Wilma Mankiller, the first woman in modern history to lead a major Native American tribe and characterized by her strong spiritual presence, worked to develop self-sufficiency in her people. Community development drove Mankiller as principal chief and resulted in increased employment, improved health care and creating programs for children in the tribe.

Mother Teresa and Princess Diana shared a friendship, much of it born of their mutual need, their calling, to reach out to those without hope. Working separately and together, they comforted and brought practical help to the poor, the sick, the disenfranchised: lepers; adults and children maimed by land mines; adults and children infected with HIV/AIDS. The blind, the aged, the dying, the destitute. Four hands — two young, two old — held out to those

I want to be remembered as the person who helped us restore faith in ourselves.
Wilma Mankiller

I have found the paradox, that if you love until it hurts, there can be no more hurt, only more love.
Mother Teresa

Nothing brings me more happiness than trying to help the most vulnerable people in society. It is a goal and an essential part of my life — a kind of destiny. Whoever is distressed can call on me. I will come running wherever they are.
Princess Diana

Queen Ka'ahumanu enfolds me in her powerful arms and fills me in an extraordinary way with the particular character of her servant-leadership, with her embodiment of the true kuhina nui.
Katherine Elberfeld, Founder,
Gabriel Center for Servant-Leadership

beyond the edges of community.

These four women — Queen Ka'ahumanu, Wilma Mankiller, Mother Teresa and Princess Diana — in different ways, in different places, in different times, held an aching world in their arms and then released it, helping it to go along better on its own than before. And in serving their people in this way, they show us once again what it really means to lead.

MOHANDAS GANDHI |

There are many causes that I am prepared to die for but no causes that I am prepared to kill for.

Mohandas Gandhi

The very name Mohandas Gandhi (1869-1948) is synonymous with non-violent peace. Immortalized as a proponent of non-partisan peace-building efforts within his native India and South Africa, the British-trained lawyer lived out his search for truth on a personal and global level by living simply in accordance with his Hindu faith. Guided by principles of truth, nonviolence, vegetarianism, simplicity and faith, Gandhi, along with the Indian National Congress, led the non-cooperation movement against the British Empire's dominant presence in India. Nonviolence, he believed, was for the strong and courageous and not to be used as a mask for cowardice. Nonviolence was not to be mistaken for passivity.

Well known as an advocate for the downtrodden "untouchable" class in India and as a denouncer of the highly codified caste system, Gandhi experienced derision and prejudice first-hand when he lived and worked in South Africa (1893-1914). Thrown from a train for failing to move to third class despite his holding a valid first-class ticket, Gandhi empathized with the mistreated Indian population residing in South Africa. To help the local Indian community solidify politically against the dominant force, he founded the Natal Indian Congress in 1894. In 1906, the government put into place an Indian registration act requiring all Indians to register their presence as foreigners, which Gandhi and his followers strongly but peacefully opposed. Public outcry against the act was so strong the South African General Jan Christiaan Smuts finally compromised. Nonviolence prevailed.

In 1915 Gandhi returned to India and soon took up his cause against the British domination of the subcontinent. For his acts and philosophy of "non-cooperation" Gandhi was arrested, tried for sedition and imprisoned in 1922 under a six-year sentence. After serving two years in prison, he was released after an operation for appendicitis.

In one of his most famous acts of resistance, Gandhi protested the British-imposed salt tax in 1930 by marching 400 kilometers to make his own salt. Several thousand followed him on his endeavor. The British imprisoned some 60,000 people in retaliation. Non-violent action shook the Empire.

With the outbreak of World War II in 1939, Gandhi and the Congress Party strengthened their position against British rule in India; the movement quickly became violent on the British end. For their acts under the Quit India movement, Gandhi and the Congress Working Committee were arrested in Bombay. Gandhi was kept at Aga Khan Palace for two years, during which he suffered the loss of his close personal secretary and of his wife. He also faced a bout of malaria and was, again, released from prison because of his failing health. The government knew the outcry would be overwhelming if Gandhi were to die inexplicably while under British watch, but self-inflicted starvation, in keeping with Gandhi's pacifistic nonviolence, would appear a suitable and just cause of death. British Prime Minister Winston Churchill remained in close contact with his advisors while Gandhi was kept under British watch. In response to Gandhi's refusing food in prison, Churchill is quoted as saying in a cabinet meeting, "I [would] keep him there and let him do as he likes," suggesting that Gandhi be allowed to starve himself to death.

Nonviolence, while peaceful in theory, created controversy and dissent in the government and people and eventually cost Gandhi his life.

In the end, one of Gandhi's dissenters chose violence. In 1948, Nathuram Godse, a Hindu radical shot and killed Gandhi on one of his nightly walks on the grounds of the Birla House in New Delhi. According to many accounts, his final words were simply, "Oh God." Jawaharlal Nehru, the first prime minister of the independent nation of India and follower of Gandhi's principles, referred to Gandhi as the father of the nation, a sentiment for which Gandhi is memorialized across the world. According to his wishes, most of his ashes were spread in many of the world's major rivers, including the Nile, Volga and Thames.

Unlike his protégés and fellow freedom fighters Desmond Tutu and Nelson Mandela, who were both very much influenced by Gandhi's stance on nonviolence, Gandhi was never awarded a Nobel Peace Prize. It is one of the great ironies of history. He was nominated for the prize five times, but the Nobel Committee excluded him because he was "not a real politician nor a humanitarian relief worker." The Nobel Foundation's director Michael Sohlam has since said that not honoring Gandhi officially is "a big regret."

But a posthumous prize isn't what Gandhi would have wanted. His legacy remains vital to peacekeepers worldwide. In January 2007, Nelson Mandela called upon Gandhi's non-violent approach to solving conflict. Referring to the Mahatma as the "sacred warrior," the South African anti-apartheid freedom fighter said, "In a world driven by violence and strife, Gandhi's message of peace and nonviolence holds the key to human survival in the 21st century…. He rightly believed in the efficacy of pitting the sole force of the *satyagraha* [nonviolent resistance] against the brute force of the oppressor and in effect converting the oppressor to the right and moral point." The sacred warrior is a servant-leader.

NELSON MANDELA & DESMOND TUTU

As I have said, the first thing is to be honest with yourself. You can never have an impact on society if you have not changed yourself … Great peacemakers are all people of integrity, of honesty, but humility.

Nelson Mandela

When reading these quotations by Nelson Mandela and Desmond Tutu you see the characteristics of the servant-leader that were the basis for these two leaders to initiate and carry out the Truth and Reconciliation process in South Africa. In the process they were very explicit in taking the injustices that were a part of apartheid, telling those stories, providing for amnesty and creating the space for forgiveness and reconciliation. It is fair to say that the Truth and Reconciliation process could not have been successful if these two men did not embody the essence of servant-leadership.

Nelson Mandela as president of South Africa initiated the Truth and Reconciliation process. It was important for the leaders during apartheid and those involved in the anti-apartheid movement to reconcile with justice. In 1995 Desmond Tutu was appointed as the Truth and Reconciliation Commission Chairperson. The aim of the Truth and Reconciliation process was to develop a culture that placed a high value on human rights to prevent recurrences of the injustices and suffering of the past. Social healing required significant sacrifices and perseverance by former oppressors, perpetrators and victims alike. Amnesty was chosen so all who committed an atrocity for political reasons, regardless of which faction that was being supported, were expected to report their actions for the purpose of documentation, be protected from prosecution and to then assume their place in society once amnesty was granted.

Desmond Tutu in his writing has contributed to the understanding of the roots of compassion, altruism and peaceful relationships. Tutu states that forgiveness is not turning a blind eye to wrongs; true reconciliation exposes the awfulness, the abuse, the pain, the hurt, the truth. He recognizes that it can even sometimes make things worse. However it was a risk worth taking because in the end only an honest confrontation with reality had a chance to bring healing.

Many books and much analysis have been written in connection with the Truth and Reconciliation process in South Africa. It is clear that the power of the process required the strong and humble servant-leadership of Desmond Tutu and Nelson Mandela. Both have been awarded the Nobel Peace Prize.

My humanity is bound up in yours, for we can only be human together.

Desmond Tutu

| MILLARD & LINDA FULLER

Millard and Linda Fuller, co-founders of Habitat for Humanity International and the Fuller Center for Housing, joined the community at Clarence Jordan's Koinonia farm in Americus, Georgia by happenstance in 1965. Stopping in to visit friends on a road trip elsewhere, the Fullers were drawn to the community atmosphere, mission and values that the community embodied. In reevaluating their marriage and commitment to Christianity, the Fullers quickly discovered a kinship in spirit with Koinonia and divested themselves of their material life. Their rebirth had begun. In 1968 Koinonia purchased 42 one-half acre plots where the newly established "Fund for Humanity" would build affordable, interest-free housing to families in need. One year later after Jordan's death in 1969, the Fullers adopted the philosophy of the Fund and took up the cause of building houses. In 1973 the Fullers tested the Fund's low-cost housing model in Zaire (now Democratic Republic of Congo). After three years in Africa the Fullers decided to return to the United States to implement their model. In September 1976 Habitat for Humanity International was born at Koinonia and would remain under the Fullers' guidance for 29 years. After the board dismissed the Fullers in 2005 over disagreements and controversy, they created the Fuller Center of Housing and based it, like Habitat, at Koinonia.

For their dedication and service to humanity, the Fullers have received almost countless awards, including the 1994 Harry S. Truman Award for Public Service and the 2002 Bronze Medallion

What the poor need is not charity but capital, not case-workers but co-workers. And what the rich need is a wise, honorable and just way of divesting themselves of their overabundance.

Clarence Jordan

from the Points of Light Foundation. Between the two of them, the Fullers have been awarded close to 60 honorary degrees. They were both prolific authors; Mr. Fuller is most noted for *Love in the Mortar Joints*, which chronicles his and Linda's lifelong mission to provide affordable housing to those in need. From their first visit to Koinonia in 1965 forward, Millard and Linda Fuller remained open to their calling, duty and sense of purpose to help those in need of affordable, sustainable housing. As Millard Fuller simply stated, "Everyone who gets sleepy at night should have a simple decent place to lay their heads, on terms they can afford to pay." Among other locations over their histories, Habitat for Humanity and the Fuller Foundation continue to build houses in the U.S., Central and Eastern Europe, Central Asia, Nigeria and El Salvador.

Under the gentle mentorship of Clarence Jordan in the wellspring that was and is the Koinonia Farm, the Fullers dedicated themselves to a cause that began on a small farm in Americus, Georgia. By giving up their known lives, these servant-leaders reinvented themselves as agents of significant change. In Millard Fuller's words, that power to affect change comes through direct action: "It's not your blue blood, your pedigree or your college degree. It's what you do with your life that counts." For living out that philosophy of philanthropy in action, former President Bill Clinton said of Millard Fuller: "(He) has literally revolutionized the concept of philanthropy." Bren Dubay, current director of Koinonia Farm, ascribes praise to the couple, rooting them in the teachings of their mentor:

> Genuine, faithful, inspiring, the salt of the earth — that's what Linda and Millard Fuller are. At Koinonia Farm, we call them friends … The Fullers truly live the words of their mentor, Koinonia founder Clarence Jordan, who wrote: 'The Scriptures should be taken out of the classroom and stained-glass sanctuary and put out under God's skies where people are toiling and crying and wondering, where the mighty events of the good news first happened, and where alone they feel at home.'

Linda and Millard Fuller have directly answered so many of those who were toiling, crying and wondering. Mr. Fuller died in February 2009.

Where are today's servant-led organizations that consciously choose to lead by serving? You'll find them everywhere. In any community or organization, whether there are two or 2,000 people, power exists. How power is distributed can greatly influence positively or negatively any efforts for alignment within the community or organization. A servant-led organization can harness the power within the group while defining roles and responsibilities and holding people accountable for achieving organizational results.

While attending a missionary school near Merrueshi, Kenya, Maasai warrior Kakuta Ole Maimai Hamisi had a dream. He wanted to go to the United States to study and bring knowledge back to Merrueshi to help his people. That dream became a decision to be made by his community.

Decisions are not taken lightheartedly by the Maasai. Each decision is held up against the question: "What will this do to our community — short term and long term?" Any resolution must meet the criteria of having "respect" for the whole community. That respect comes first and last and can perhaps help to explain how some of the familiar aspects of our western world, such as jealousy, greed, sarcasm, criticism, self-centeredness and fear of failure, are very rare for this Maasai community. They have little or no crime, theft, rape or other intra-community violence. Issues such as "who has the most cattle or goats or pots and tea cups" do not become

He lives in harmony with The Creator and with the earth; he knows who he is and what his place is in the great scheme of things; he experiences abundance everywhere.

Kakuta Ole Maimai Hamisi

divisive. Even at the very personal level, the individual Maasai man, woman or even child, would never think about doing something that would threaten the well-being of the community. The Maasai are truly servants to each other.

In this situation, Kakuta's warrior brothers and cousins sold cows, sheep and goats, the only three kinds of animals the Maasai eat, to help make his dream a reality for all of them. The next step was to learn what school would be available to him and how to earn additional money to support him throughout this ambitious effort. Gathering information of this sort is not an easy task. The closest computer for internet surfing was a six-hour walk away.

Searching for financial assistance, Kakuta learned that the University of Washington in Seattle had a work-study position available at the Woodland Park Zoo, and he chose to go there. His job: helping to design a true-to-life exhibit featuring his brother and sister animals of the African savanna. He was just the man for the job and has been spending two- or three-month blocks of time helping design the exhibits and caring for the kinds of animals with which he ran wild throughout his life. Kakuta commutes back and forth from Kenya while he is studying and working at the zoo. Kakuta transferred to the Evergreen State University to get access to its more flexible course structure and graduated with a degree in international studies. He also holds a master's degree from the School for International Training at Brattleboro, Vermont.

What makes Kakuta's story so compelling is that while a few other Maasai had gone away for schooling, no one had gotten a graduate degree. Nor had any who left and discovered the new world come back to be with their people. Kakuta's promise to return to lead his people into this technological world coming at them like a freight train continued to rule his decision making.

As a junior elder, Kakuta is a respected leader. During his absence the power structure in his community adjusts, and other warriors make necessary decisions. When he returns the other warriors step aside and allow their respected brother to take the lead. This back-and-forth flow of leadership appears seamless because of their shared values. There is no question of what leadership should involve.

Decisions are made for the good of everyone. The Maasai act as if they are "stewards" of what is in their world. Any child or adult who comes inside their circle is considered a member of the community. There is no word for "orphan" in their language. A sentence worse than death for them would involve being ostracized from the group. They go far in being open and honest with each other because they know they will never be separated from one another unless they do something that indicates their selfishness is more important than the community.

One might expect that Kakuta would do as many others have done when they become educated in the developed world — to stay there and live an "easier" life. But when John Scherer, an organization development consultant, took a group of business people to Merrueshi to learn about this community and Kakuta's leadership, this is what he said about Kobole, a typical brother-warrior:

> He has everything he needs: a community that cares about him and his well-being; a band of brothers that would die for him — and he for them. He lives in harmony with The Creator (the Maasai word for God), and with the earth; he knows who he is and what his place is in the great scheme of things; he experiences abundance everywhere. He is confident; self-esteem is not an issue for him. He knows when to use his power and when to be gentle. He has respect for his elders, and is respected by them. Except for the drought that threatens their life now, he and his community find everything they need in the world around them. He is happy. Not just superficially happy, but deeply satisfied and fulfilled. Except for learning, he does not hanker for more of anything. He has what our clients — and we, too — are seeking in our lives.

Robert Greenleaf would have been honored to know Kakuta and call him colleague.

The Maasai lack resources and at times face drought that includes the loss of cattle, an extremely valuable commodity for the Maasai. What they lack in resources, they make up for in their sense of community, which gives them an experience of abundance. They are a servant-leadership community.

What is it that Kakuta feels his community needs to learn? The Maasai face the changes that every indigenous people before them have faced — being assimilated into a more mechanical and/

or technological world. They need to learn how to deal with that impact on them and what they can hang onto and even offer to the rest of society. Kakuta's master's thesis is intended to help him and his people deal with these inevitable changes and retain the beauty and grace of being a servant-leadership community.

Community
Questionnaire

What have we to learn from the Maasai? Consider these questions:

What would your organization be like if people put the long-term well-being of the community first and last, such as all the stakeholders, including customers, employees, vendors and competitors?

What if your organization's culture reinforced people holding what they had — status, perks, power, position — "lightly," as if they were taking care of it on behalf of the entire community?

What if there were no word for orphan in our communities?

What if your organization saw that everyone, each and every person — because of their uniqueness, not in spite of it — had a contribution to make?

What if your organization cared so much about community that it would not rest until it had found a way to connect each person to that community and empowered them to contribute?

What would happen if you decided to work toward making your organization/community truly servant-led?

SERVANT-LEADER | ORGANIZATIONS

In addition to the Maasai community, numerous universities and other organizations have had success implementing servant-leadership programs, including:

- Viterbo University in La Crosse, Wisconson, offers a master's degree in servant-leadership. The only master's degree in the world focused specifically on servant-leadership, this program brings together people who aspire to leadership positions in church, community and business.

• Seton Hall University in South Orange, New Jersey, incorporates a strong servant-leadership component into its students' education. The school has its own department dedicated toward the mission – The Center of Vocation and Servant Leadership.

• The Episcopal School of Texas uses "educating servant-leaders ..." as a slogan.

• Concordia University, a Lutheran Christian university in Seward, Nebraska, has incorporated servant-leadership into its curriculum under the slogan "Preparing servant-leaders for church and world." Concordia students are required to take a servant-leadership practicum in which they perform a sixty-hour service project.

• In 2004, a servant-leadership program was established by the Milwaukee School of Engineering from an endowment by Dr. Richard Pieper, establishing MSOE as the first and only university with a chair position in servant-leadership.

• Gonzaga University in Spokane, Washington, offers on campus and online a strong program for a master's in organizational leadership that focuses on the philosophy and practice of servant-leadership.

• CEO Netweavers, a nonprofit organization in Dallas, Texas, has more than 300 CEO/COO members whose vision is to transform business and enrich lives through servant-leadership.

Servant-leader organizations have been in the top 10 on Fortune 500's list of "The 100 Best Companies To Work for in America" since its inception in 1998. We will take an in-depth look at five **organizations practicing servant-leadership today**:

• The Housing Facilities Department of the University of Michigan, Ann Arbor
• Southwest Airlines
• Nordstrom
• TDIndustries, a Dallas-based company that designs and installs heating and air-conditioning units
• IMPACT Silver Spring, a community organization

Many of these organizations decided to apply servant-leadership principles to their organizations after reading Robert Greenleaf, but others arrived at the same place intuitively and later found that Greenleaf's ideas gave language to their emerging identity.

What about the bottom line? Companies in the Fortune 500's "Best Places To Work" list average a 50 percent higher profit margin than competitors of similar size. But Jack Lowe Jr., president of TDIndustries, cautions, "If you go into this with the motive to make more money, it won't work. If you go into it to build people and a great organization, you will make more money over the long run."

THE UNIVERSITY OF MICHIGAN'S HOUSING FACILITIES DEPARTMENT

The Housing Facilities Department is responsible for maintenance of all buildings and residential housing at the Ann Arbor campus. 243 housing facilities staff service an arena that encompasses 4.6 million square feet and 16,000 residents.

In the late 1980s the director of the Housing Facilities Department had a vision. George SanFacon wanted to co-create "an appropriate workplace experience" for himself and others – one that would promote the growth and well-being of both those involved and those affected. After considerable research and a few false starts, he finally decided that the best way to accomplish his goal was to abolish the traditional, authoritarian boss/subordinate management model in favor of one based on shared governance and mutual vulnerability. In doing so, he relinquished his unilateral power and authority over others and adopted servant-leadership.

In early 1992, a unique round-table format was proposed and adopted that established a council of equals to govern the organization using consensus decision making. Over the years, this framework evolved into an integrated network of overlapping teams that lead and manage the enterprise, enabling the department to achieve significantly higher levels of performance. The group follows the decision-making model called "primus inter pares" that translates as "first among equals." Each person in a decision group is equal, but the one who happens to be chairperson that day, or that week or year, is the "first among equals."

George SanFacon talks about his philosophy of "promoting human well being and engaging the spirit" in *Awake at Work: Concepts and Principles for Creating Better Workplaces and a Better*

World. He says:

> In most workplaces, things like quality, productivity and profit are thought of and pursued as primary outcomes and results. People, on the other hand, are thought of and treated as means to those ends — biological resources that are manipulated in order to achieve desired outcomes. The following is based on a different way of thinking — that 'work exists for the person as much as the person exists for work ... [that] the business exists as much to provide meaningful work to the person as it exists to provide a product and service to the customer.' From this perspective, work should be a vehicle of growth, enjoyment and service for us. When it is, the power of the human spirit is unleashed, encompassing the intangibles of morale, commitment, joy, love and energy. The natural byproducts of such an alignment and experience include higher levels of productivity, creativity and quality.

SanFacon identifies the benefits of living the model:

- Resources are freely shared across units;
- Turnover is extremely low;
- Outstanding performers from elsewhere watch for opportunities to join the enterprise;
- Feedback on the quality of services is viewed as information rather than as a threat;
- Performance assessment has become a journey in self-awareness rather than defensiveness;
- Customer satisfaction levels have increased;
- Financial performance has improved; and
- There is more joy, caring, fun, understanding and support for members, both personally and professionally.

With their principle of shared management, the group governance and management structure creates a powerful "container" within which continuous improvement and systems change, as well as personal and organizational transformation, are sustained. Key elements of this open framework and shared governance system include the following:

nontraditional reporting relationships: Instead of having a traditional, one-on-one reporting relationship, individual managers report to their team (or to the Council) as a whole. Over time, participants lose their fear of reprisals for being honest, and "undiscussables" become discussable. People come to see that both the team members and the enterprise become vulnerable when problems or weaknesses are not acknowledged and addressed.

consensus decision making: The governance and management teams operate solely by consensus decision making, minimizing the formation of factions and win-lose dynamics. Consensus is defined as "every member being willing to accept and fully support the decision as a good one for the group and enterprise, even if it doesn't represent their personal first choice or preference."

clear boundary conditions: The department's mission, goals and values are clearly stated, and all agree that shared power and authority are to be used to further the collective purpose of the enterprise. Individuals sign a charter that states they will work in good faith, and to the best of their ability, to accomplish the mission and goals.

performance and good faith effort distinguished: In the traditional model, individuals are continually at risk and vulnerable if their performance is inadequate. In this model, individual performance issues are handled by self-correction, compensating actions of team members or a combination thereof. The team members stand together; as long as an individual is working in good faith, he or she can count on the continued support of the other members.

an "open book" system: There are few, if any, secrets. Departmental budgets, individual and team performance and individual merit pay and salaries are all determined using team-based processes. Performance assessment and feedback systems provide information to measure the quality of services, quantity of work done and the performance levels of both individuals and teams. Agendas and meeting minutes for all teams are shared across the entire department.

effective linkages: The first among equals connects and integrates the governing Council with the Management Teams. Linking consists of continuously engaging in both the Council and Team arenas, thereby creating a dynamic organizational network. Other types of linkages used include task forces, ad hoc groups and standing subgroups for specific functional areas.

choice: Fulfilling governance roles is a privilege and an act of service for the common good. Managers are therefore given the freedom to choose whether or not they want to give up their traditional one-on-one reporting relationship to share management responsibilities. With only one exception, the department's thirty-five supervisory, managerial and professional staff members have chosen a team-based rather than a one-on-one reporting relationship.

Southwest Airlines started in 1971 with Rollin King and Herb Kelleher having a cocktail while discussing Rollin's idea for an airline that would fly among three Texas cities. Today Southwest is the largest domestic carrier in terms of passengers carried, serving over one hundred destinations with more than 46,000 employees.

At Southwest Airlines, its Customers and Employees are the top priority. They always capitalize the "C" in "Customer" and the "E" in "Employee," and paychecks are signed "From Our Customers." These habits visibly remind Southwest of what is most important in the customer service business. "Positively Outrageous Service" is stressed from Day One to all Employees — from ground operations agents to flight attendants. It is not unusual to see a vice president "pitch in" to help a ramp agent load bags, or a station manager go out of his or her way to make sure customers are comfortable. Every employee recognizes the goal of excellent customer service, regardless of rank or job description. It is this system-wide dedication to Positively Outrageous Service that has won Southwest tremendous industry recognition. Since 1997, Fortune magazine has included Southwest on its list of America's Most Admired Companies. Southwest's commitment to its employees is:

> We are committed to provide our Employees a stable work environment with equal opportunity for learning and personal growth. Creativity and innovation are encouraged for improving

| SOUTHWEST AIRLINES

Southwest's culture has been its competitive advantage. You can't put it on a balance sheet, but it's something close to priceless.

Fortune, May 16, 2005

the effectiveness of Southwest Airlines. Above all, Employees will be provided the same concern, respect and caring attitude within the organization that they are expected to share externally with every Southwest Customer.

Besides being smart, efficient and dedicated, Southwest Airlines' more than 46,000 Employees are "required" to be one more thing: FUN! Humor is an essential element of Southwest's success, and this attitude comes straight from the top. Herb Kelleher, the Fun-LUVing, off-the-cuff former chairman of the board, has, among other things, dressed up like Elvis, given out whiskey with airline tickets and settled an industry dispute with an arm-wrestling competition. It is from such unique leadership that Southwest's extraordinary corporate culture has evolved, and the motto "We take the competition seriously, but we don't take ourselves seriously" has been fully embraced. Employees routinely dress up and decorate offices for holidays, tell silly jokes and even sing in-flight instructions to customers. So how do they find employees who fit the Southwest mold? Each employee is carefully chosen from more than 250,000 applications that Southwest receives each year, and attitude is the essential attribute that Southwest recruiters look for in each new employee.

Herb Kelleher is cited as a natural servant-leader who surrounds himself with a diverse team of servant-leaders. "I have always believed that the best leader is the best server," says Kelleher. "And if you're a servant, by definition, you're not controlling. We try to value each person individually and to be cognizant of them as human beings — not just people who work for our company."

Southwest discovered Robert Greenleaf's servant-leadership writings well after they had established a servant-leader culture. Herb says Greenleaf's ideas "give language" to what they were doing anyway.

On March 21, 2005, *Fortune* magazine published "The Best Advice I Ever Got." Herb Kelleher founder and former chairman of Southwest Airlines, said, "Respect people for who they are, not for what their titles are." In the article Herb explains:

> I'd say my mother made more of a difference to me than anyone else did. I know that's a conventional and perhaps mundane answer, but there were so many things I learned from her. One

piece of advice that always stuck in my mind is that people should be respected and trusted as people, not because of their position or title. Frequently, position or title did not reflect the true merits of a person. I got a lesson confirming that almost immediately because there was a gentleman [in our town] who was the head of a financial institution. He was always dressed immaculately, and he gave the impression of being a very upstanding guy. Well, he was indicted, convicted and sent to jail for embezzling. Thanks to her advice, in the business world I try not to judge anyone by superficial standards. I try to approach them with an open mind. I'm very interested in their ideas. You don't have to have a doctorate to have an idea. You ought to be open to listening to people. Show that you care about them as individuals, not just as workers. You know how some people are always looking over your shoulder to see if there's somebody more important behind you? Well, one of the things that I've tried to do — if I'm talking to a person, that person is the only person in the world while we're talking. They're owed that. Besides, they're usually fascinating. Getting together with the people of Southwest is one of the most rewarding and exciting things in my business life.

President Emerita Colleen Barrett turned heads at an address to the Texas Society of Association Executives' annual conference when she used the words family, love and Golden Rule behavior in describing the success of Southwest Airlines. "Our entire focus is culture based — a focus on the family," Barrett said.

It's a popular theme these days, but when we were young and energetic, we made the decision in the late '60s — we had no area of expertise — to concentrate on what we knew we did well, and that was treat people with respect and use Golden Rule behavior. We knew if we did that, did it well and held people accountable, we would be successful.

But Barrett cautioned executives that a familial environment can't be created overnight and can't be canned. "Caring can't be a program or an agenda," she said. "It has to be an everyday thing — so much a part of you that you don't even think about it. You have to know when someone is bothered, when a great performer is suddenly not. We run our organization that way." All work and no play make life dull. At least that is what Barrett told executives attending the conference. "There is nothing wrong with enjoying what you do every day," she said. "We make our own fun."

NORDSTROM |

People will work hard when they are given the freedom to do the job the way they think it should be done, when they treat customers the way they like to be treated. When you take away their incentive and start giving them rules — boom! You've killed their creativity.

Jim Nordstrom

Nordstrom is famous for its customer service. It is also a company that often speaks of servant-leadership and truly believes that it is the role of each leader to support and serve the efforts of the front-line employees. New employees are given a copy of the famous Nordstrom's Employee Handbook — a single five by eight inch gray card containing 75 words:

Welcome to Nordstrom
We're glad to have you with our Company.

Our number one goal is to provide outstanding customer service. Set both your personal and professional goals high. We have great confidence in your ability to achieve them.

Nordstom Rules:
Rule #1: Use your good judgement in all situations.

There will be no additional rules.

Please feel free to ask your department manager, store manager or divisional general manager any question at any time.

Nordstrom's Employee

Handbook

Nordstrom gives people the freedom to do whatever it takes to make the customer happy, as long as it's legal. If you boil down the Nordstrom system to its essence, it's that Nordstrom gives the people on the sales floor the freedom to make decisions — and management supports them in those decisions.   Nordstrom continually reinforces this attitude by spreading stories of customer service that are above and beyond the call of duty. In the Nordstrom culture, these stories are called "heroics."

One heroics story from *The Nordstrom Way: The Insider Story of America's #1 Service Company*, by Robert Spector, is of a customer who fell in love with a pair of burgundy, pleated Donna Karan slacks that had just gone on sale at the Nordstrom store in downtown Seattle. But the store was out of her size, and the sales associate was unable to track down a pair at the five other Nordstrom stores in the Seattle area. Aware that the same slacks were available across the street at a competitor, the associate secured some petty cash from her department manager, marched across the street to the rival department store where she bought the slacks at full price, returned to Nordstrom and then sold them to the customer for the marked-down Nordstrom price. While Nordstrom didn't make money on that sale, it was an investment in promoting the loyalty of an appreciative customer who, more than likely, thought of Nordstrom for her next purchase.

As these stories are spread throughout the organization, employees see that the people who run the company encourage, honor and reward outstanding acts of customer service. Management is not just giving lip service to customer service but actually doing something about it. They are living out the principles of servant-leadership.

Nordstrom has put these values into practice with an organizational commitment to put the customer first. In a standard organizational hierarchy, the president/CEO and the board of directors are at the top, then the senior level managers, divisional or middle managers, low-level managers or supervisors and then the workers at the bottom.

Traditional Corporate Hierarchy

This **traditional model** has been used for many years and its strengths include:

- order;
- stability;
- predictability; and
- centralized power.

However, this model tends to be bureaucratic and designed so individuals follow the rules and follow a chain of command. Power and responsibility flow from the top down. Those at the bottom have the least power, and managers in the middle tend to use their organizational power to satisfy those above them and at the top of the pyramid.

The problem the traditional model causes in a customer service environment, for example, is that workers who are the people closest to the customer and understand their wants and needs are often not empowered to meet those needs. However, those who have the most power to make service-related decisions that affect customers are the senior staff farthest away from customers in the hierarchy. If customers' wants and needs do not mesh very well with the goals defined at the top of the pyramid, there is no effective way for those at the bottom to influence those goals.

In contrast to the traditional pyramid model, today's global economy is requiring organizations that are:

- flexible;
- adaptable;
- quickly responsive; and
- creative.

Nordstrom is often held up as the ultimate example of superior customer service, with staff going to extreme measures to satisfy the needs of customers. And Nordstrom does not want just to satisfy its customers — it wants to delight them by going beyond expectations.

The key to delighting customers is Nordstrom's famous "inverted pyramid." The top position is occupied by customers, with the sales and support people serving them. What makes this structure unique is that every tier of the inverted pyramid works to support the sales staff, not the other way around. Inverting the pyramid empowers staff by allowing them to use their common sense and good judgment to provide good customer service. It also moves responsibility and decision making to the people who are in contact with customers. Nordstrom gives the people on the sales floor the freedom to make decisions, and their managers support them in those decisions. Sales people are judged on their performance, not their obedience to orders, and individual creativity is a byproduct of freedom.

Nordstrom's Inverted Pyramid

Jim's brother John Nordstrom held a liberating vision when he inverted the pyramid and recognized that real power does not come from a "command and control" authoritative structure. He knew that serving the customer was most important and freeing people closest to the customer to use their best judgment to make the customer happy was a "win-win" for the customer, the employee and the company.

TDIndustries has more experience with a servant-leadership culture than any corporation in the United States. TDIndustries is a heating and plumbing contracting firm that has consistently ranked in the top 10 of *Fortune* magazine's 100 Best Companies to Work for in America. The founder, Jack Lowe Sr., came upon Robert Greenleaf's essay "The Servant as Leader" in the early 1970s and began to distribute copies of it to his employees. When people become grounded in servant-leadership, trust grows, and the foundation for organizational excellence is established, Lowe believes.

Jack Lowe Jr. continued to use servant-leadership as the company's guiding philosophy. Even today, any TDPartner, as TDI employees are called, who supervises even one person must go through training in servant-leadership. In addition, all new employees continue to receive copies of "The Servant as Leader," and TDIndustries has developed elaborate training modules designed to encourage the understanding and practice of servant-leadership.

TDIndustries is now a part of *Fortune* magazine's 100 Best

| TDINDUSTRIES

Until someone has been in our work environment where the individual is valued, encouraged, challenged, guided, given freedom to perform and is loved, it is difficult to comprehend the power of the trust that exists here.

Jack Lowe Jr., Managing Partner until 2005

Companies to Work for Hall of Fame — a distinction that only 22 other companies hold. TDIndustries espouses that "Servant Leaders are active listeners ... they elicit trust ... and share power." Guiding their relationships with customers, suppliers, communities, and among themselves, **TDIndustries' Basic Values** are their most important characteristics:

- Concern for and belief in individual human beings
- Valuing individual differences
- Honesty
- Building trusting relationships
- Fairness
- Responsible behavior
- High standards of business ethics
- Long-term goals — we do not seize short-term benefits to the detriment of our long-term mission.
- Continuous, intense people-development efforts, including substantial training budgets.
- Investment in tools, equipment and facilities that enable us to better accomplish our mission.

It is one thing for a boss to say to their employees, "I work for you." But being willing to submit yourself to a vote of your employees whether or not you stay shows just one little glimpse into why TDIndustries is a model servant-leadership organization. More than 900 employees and recent retirees own 100 percent of the company. No single individual controls more than 3 percent of the company's stock. In fact, the entire senior management team controls less than 25 percent of the stock. Employees feel treated as full members regardless of their position. Health insurance premiums are indexed to income; the more one makes, the more one pays. After three years, employees receive an astonishing 12 weeks off at full pay.

Servant-leadership is at the heart of TDI's business theory, which is based on a metaphor of the construction industry in which they work. A building is erected in steps. Accordingly, so too must an ethical corporate culture. Servant-leadership in TDI's practice is the essential process for preparing a firm, bedrock site upon which to build. This provides the necessary grounding for laying down a foundation of trust. Trust, then, undergirds four key ascending pillars:

- continuous learning;
- shared commitment;
- authentic diversity; and
- strategic planning.

These pillars, in turn, support a canopy community of powerful trusting partners. The partners work together to delight their customers. Satisfied customers result in business success, which further reinforces the community of powerful, trusting partners. This virtuous cycle is reinforced by constantly maintaining a culture of trust, service, quality and learning. The firm's philosophy was tested in the late 1980s when the industry had virtually collapsed, and banks were deep in losses as well. Unable to raise $16 million to stay afloat, employees risked their retirements to keep the firm alive. In less than a year, TDI recovered.

In 1998 the Montgomery County, Maryland., Executive's Silver Spring Redevelopment Steering Committee had just completed a lengthy process of deciding how best to revitalize its community. The process involved numerous agreements and disagreements, proposals that were accepted only to be later rejected, disillusionments and finally resolution. One of the members of this group was Frankie Blackburn, a young female lawyer who had spent a number of years working on affordable housing in the Silver Spring area.

|IMPACT SILVER SPRING

    Throughout the process, a sub-group of people kept reminding the Redevelopment Steering Committee that leadership within Silver Spring was as important an issue as physical restructuring. The agreed-upon revitalization project included plans to change and improve the physical structure of Silver Spring by replacing old buildings and businesses with newer ones and promised to bring about greater economic growth and services for residents. However, it had not taken into account the issue of existing leadership. Silver Spring is a very diverse community, but a large majority of leadership came from a dominant group of mostly white, single-family homeowners. A pivotal victory for the sub-group within the Advisory Committee was the inclusion of a recommendation within the final report that the county executive would commit further exploration of a "Leadership

Institute" as a continuing feature of Silver Spring's redevelopment. As the group exploring the institute evolved, Frankie Blackburn emerged as a leader — first as an informal convener and then eventually as the Executive Director. She, in particular, paid close attention from the beginning of this phase to the importance of working closely with the Silver Spring Regional Government Center.

Frankie gathered together six to eight people who were knowledgeable either in the inner workings of Silver Spring, representatives of diverse populations and/or experienced in leadership and organizational development. That first group of volunteers met weekly for a whole year before the first leadership program was established. There was a high level of collaboration and shared decision-making within the group. Each person's ideas were heard and considered equally. Frankie was truly committed to seeing that people from all walks of life have an opportunity to share their inherent gifts of leadership and represent themselves and people like them. The group strived for a balance of power in its inner workings. At one point the group came to loggerheads around what was suspected to be diversity issues, and an outside consultant was brought in to help the group process what was going on so that they could move forward.

The first training program, following a brief pilot program, began in 1999. It was called the Community Empowerment and Involvement Program. Participants were intentionally selected to guarantee diversity within the group. The thrust of the nine-month program focused on building leadership capacities. The group diversity maximized everyone's learning. One example of intergroup networking was when a female participant who headed a senior citizen support network agreed to write grants to help an Ethiopian participant in his efforts to publish an ethnic newspaper, in exchange for her organization's entry into the Ethiopian community. From the very beginning the group began taking on the stewardship qualities of a servant-leader community, i.e., the commitment to serving the needs of others.

The servant-leader seeks to be effective at building consensus rather than trying to coerce compliance. This was evident on Frankie's part as she worked with the group in the process of creating a board of directors and choosing the name "IMPACT Silver Spring" for the organization. IMPACT continues to be a nonprofit organization that works to build a thriving multicultural community. Through training and support, IMPACT teaches how to build trusting relationships among diverse people to develop a shared vision for the community's future. IMPACT's cutting-edge programs, led by a team of talented facilitators and educators, work by engaging community members, building awareness in current leaders, developing leaders through training and support and sparking action through collaboration between diverse individuals and groups. To date hundreds of enthusiastic and committed individuals have participated, and their leadership in schools, neighborhoods and communities has expanded growth and problem resolution in the community. They focus on four primary areas:

Neighborhood IMPACT: a nine-month leadership program for renters, which teaches essential skills for working with diverse people and groups and provides a framework for collaborative action.

IMPACT in the Schools: works with parents, schools and communities to build successful multicultural schools and to bridge the growing achievement gap between white and immigrant and minority children.

Lasting IMPACT: a leadership network for graduates of IMPACT programs, includes leadership development, peer support, mentoring, incubating new community projects and community action.

IMPACT Connections: provides facilitation and technical support linking emerging leaders to established leaders and building bridges across organizations.

The organization and those who have been involved have received the following recognitions:

> • The Linowes Leadership Award for Unsung Heroes, from the Community Foundation of the National Capital Area, which was awarded to Frankie Blackburn.
> • The Linowes Leadership Award was awarded to three graduates: Agnes Kariuki, Hoan Dang and Mary McCurty.

• The Volunteer of the Year award from the Greater Silver Spring Chamber of Commerce was given to founding board members Jim Henkelman-Bahn and Jackie Bahn-Henkelman.

• IMPACT in the Schools won the Henry L. Dixon Community Service Awards from the Community Action Board of Montgomery County and the Distinguished Service to Public Education Award from the Montgomery County Board of Education.

• IMPACT Silver Spring was selected as one of the best small charities in the Greater Washington region, as featured in the 2007-08 Catalogue for Philanthropy.

IMPACT Silver Spring is without a doubt a servant-leader community organization. Frankie Blackburn is without a doubt a servant-leader. She is always willing to bring to the surface aspects from her own experience that may be helpful. When she is aware that she is attached to her own ideas, she is willing to step back and listen to others. She lets people know what is fearful to her and puts her trust in others as well as committing resources accordingly. Frankie lives her ethics: fighting but fighting fairly for her beliefs, principles and approaches to shift the base of Silver Spring community leadership to one more representative of its cultural diversity. She continues to be a catalyst for Silver Spring's becoming a thriving multicultural community.

Now that you have read these stories, we invite you to answer the following questions and apply them to your own organization.

Organization
Questionnaire

If you think of your organization of a garden,

How could a garden metaphor work for your organization?

What new seeds would benefit the organization?

What cycles, processes and/or standards need to change to match the servant-leader model?

What needs to be done to improve teamwork?

How could your organization prepare the soil in terms of its values and principles?

As we realign our organizations and governance with our belief systems — that view others with integrity and rights to contribute and serve in a world desperately needing more harmony — we can pay particular attention to the qualities of people applying for positions in our organizations. The following list of questions can serve as a guideline for the interviewers to ask during the hiring process. You may choose not to use them all, and you may choose to add your own, but these will give you a start. These suggestions will help to answer the question: *What are we really looking for when we scrutinize someone's appropriate fit for a position — whether it is for an organization or a political appointment?* We do not stop with the academic qualifications. We want more:

- Who are they and how they have served in the past?
- Do they really know themselves and are honest with themselves?
- What is their Emotional Intelligence (EQ) as well as their IQ?
- Do they really listen to others?
- Are they open to learning?
- Have they and will they use power ethically?
- Have they and will they embrace diversity?
- Would they inspire others and deserve others' trust?
- Do they possess intuition and foresight?
- Can they collaborate and include others' thinking in decision making?
- Are they open to critical feedback, and are they self-reflective?
- Can they deal with paradox in a healthy manner?

Time after time studies have shown that the leader with these characteristics will satisfy performance requirements over individuals who may even have had more on-the-job experience and/or a higher IQ but does not possess these servant-leader qualities. Such an approach will hold our organizations in good stead in times of success and also in times of stress.

Leadership theories have shifted over the years. Early theorists believed that leaders were born with the qualities they needed to be effective. Experience has taught us that innate qualities can be enhanced by knowledge and skill development. People can become servant-leaders. The challenge is to hire personnel who are open to the servant-leader model and then develop their skills.

a liberating vision

Holding a liberating vision for the organization is a common characteristic of a servant-leader. He or she sees a destination and excites others about the journey. However, in a servant-leader organization the vision is embedded in the organization itself and not just in the leader. Before the leader of a group in the organization can articulate the vision, it is important to be clear about the values that are held in the organization. The vision needs to be in alignment with the values. Once the values and vision are articulated, the mission will be clear.

The following activity can include all members of an organization. It has been used with small organizations as well as with organizations consisting of thousands of people or a subgroup within a large organization. Typically when a subgroup within a large organization gathers for this purpose, the group consists of senior management. However, an appropriate subgroup can include a cross section of all the stakeholders in the organization. For illustration purposes the following activity is designed for a group of 100 participants representing one organization and working with a facilitator. It can be adapted for other size groups.

Identifying Values, Vision and Mission Activity

Each participant is randomly assigned a two-digit number (00, 01 … 98, 99). Participants begin the activity by sitting at a numbered table that matches the first of the two digits.

The space must be large enough to allow the free circulation of the people who are engaged in the activity. It should be set up with ten tables numbered (0,1 ... 8, 9) for ten people each. An easel with chart paper and markers is available at each table.

These tasks are best spread over a couple of days. However, an abbreviated process is also possible. One way to speed up the process for large groups is to use instant voting by all participants if the computer technology is available for each person.

storytelling: (Task 1) The first task for each of the ten people who are gathered at the tables is to share a brief story about a time in his or her life in the organization when he or she felt most alive, creative, excited, successful and enthusiastic. After the round of storytelling the group will, drawing on their experiences, determine the life-giving forces that represent the organization at its best and record these on the chart paper. This way of beginning is in the spirit of Appreciative Inquiry, which focuses on what is working well in the group or organization.

moving to new table groups: The participants now form cross-groups by moving to join a group at the table whose number matches the second of the two digits the participant was assigned.

determining organizational values: (Task 2) This second task is to identify the values that are inherent in the life-giving forces identified by the first table groups. The groups will prioritize their lists of values and select their top five values. These values can be written on separate cards so they can be easily reordered.

determining the final organizational values: One person from each table will be invited to bring these top five values written on separate cards to a circle of chairs with an easel and chart paper in the middle of the other ten table groups. The cards can be posted with duplicates clustered. This inner circle of chairs forms a fishbowl for determining the final organizational values based on the clustered cards. An empty chair will be provided for any of the other participants to bring his or her perspective into the group For a group of this size microphones will be necessary in the fishbowl so all can hear the discussion and come to the empty chair as they are moved to do that. The product of this discussion in the fishbowl will either be the final organizational values or a draft to be finalized later by a smaller group.

determining the organizational vision: (Task 3) The third task is to identify the organizational vision that captures the life-giving forces identified earlier and is consistent with the values espoused in Task 2. One way to do this is to have each of the table groups for Task 2 develop a provocative vision statement that would stretch the organization and record the statement on the chart paper.

determining the final organizational vision: These ten provocative vision statements can then be posted for a gallery walk where everyone walks around and votes with a stick-on dot for the one he or she believes best captures the direction for the organization. Before a final decision is made the fishbowl might be used again to refine the wording and to be sure that the vision reflects the life-giving forces identified in the organization as well as the values already determined. The product of this discussion in the fishbowl will either be the final organizational vision or a draft to be finalized by a small group in the same manner as the organizational values.

determining the organizational mission: (Task 4) Now that the values and the vision have been determined, the mission follows naturally. One way to approach this is to form groups representing different parts of the organization. For instance, the senior management of the organization might develop the overall mission statement at the same time as separate units or interest areas work on their mission statements. The work on the mission should grow out of the overall values and vision.

But the fuller nature desires to be an agent, to create, and not merely to look on: strong love hungers to bless, and not merely to behold blessing. And while there is warmth enough in the sun to feed an energetic life, there will still be ... [people] to feel, 'I am lord of this moment's change, and will charge it with my soul.'"

George Eliot

Daniel Deronda

[T]he essence of belief is doubt, the essence of reality is questioning. The essence of Time is Flow, not Fix. The essence of faith is the knowledge that all flows and that everything must change.

Thomas Wolfe

You Can't Go Home Again

The first peace ... comes from within the souls of [human beings] when they realize their relationship, their oneness, with the universe and all its powers, and when they realize that at the center of the universe dwells the Sacred, and that this center is really everywhere, it is within each of us.

Black Elk

Sacred Pipe

[A]t bottom we know that the throne which the people support, stands, and that when that support is removed, nothing in this world can save it.

Mark Twain

Personal Recollections of Joan of Arc

I have the satisfaction of knowing that it is all right; that everybody else is one way or other served in much the same way — either in a physical or metaphysical point of view, that is; and so the universal thump is passed round, and all hands should rub each other's shoulder-blades, and be content.

Herman Melville

Moby-Dick

[H]e allowed himself to be swayed by his conviction that human beings are not born once and for all on the day their mothers give birth to them, but that life obliges them over and over again to give birth to themselves.

Gabriel García Márquez

Love in the Time of Cholera

servant-leadership in film and literature

As we have seen throughout this workbook, we can find servant-leaders and evidence of servant-leadership in many places and showing up in many different ways. We are including here a few movies that demonstrate aspects of servant-leadership, and we invite you to look for examples as you watch movies either on your own or with a group. Such an activity can trigger fun topics for discussion groups, in which you and others talk more about servant-leadership, what it means in your lives and how you can engage its power even more fully every day.

Der Untergang (Downfall) |
(2004)

Downfall shows us another side of Hitler's dictatorship by telling part of the story through his secretary, Traudl Junge. Hitler lived out his last days in a bunker with his mistress, and Junge was well aware of all that was happening. She knew young children were fighting in the war and that innocent men, women and children were being murdered by Hitler's army.

What does this movie say about mutual accountability, questioning authority and being willing to see what is going on around us?

What other aspects of servant-leadership can you identify in this movie?

Brubaker (1980) |

As new prison warden Henry Brubaker goes undercover in a state prison to investigate conditions there, he observes events that defy comprehension. Brubaker witnesses inside criminal activity ranging from inmates running a "prisoner slavery ring" to having to pay for "good" food. Hoping for change and to turn things around, Brubaker has and made enemies throughout the community. He has no idea that he has angered the very people he hopes would help him, but they are the ones who have been benefitting from the criminal activity within the prison system.

What does this movie say about being an agent of change?

What other aspects of servant-leadership can you identify in this movie?

Nature is the main character of this film from cinematographer and editor Ron Fricke. Although this film has no script, it is full of amazing music, photography and visuals from around the world. It depicts images that range from post war to peace, beauty and spirituality.

| *Baraka* (1993)

What does this movie say about the importance of simply "being" rather than focusing to a large extent on "doing?"

What other aspects of servant-leadership can you identify in this movie?

This docudrama, directed by George Clooney, depicts CBS journalist Edward R. Murrow's decision to stand up to Sen. Joseph McCarthy, who was on a mission to rid the country of communism. In this Oscar-nominated film, Murrow maintained fearless determination as he fought to expose the lies and corruption committed by McCarthy.

| *Good Night, and Good Luck* (2005)

What does this movie say about the importance of open discussion and freedom of communication?

What other aspects of servant-leadership can you identify in this movie?

Whale Rider is the story of a Maori girl, Paikea Apirana (Pai), standing up to traditional beliefs to become the tribe leader. The Maori tribe, New Zealand's indigenous population, have always been led by the first-born male. Pai struggles with her grandfather for the right to become the first female chief.

| *Whale Rider* (2002)

Name some examples of Pai's leadership and why they are significant.

What other aspects of servant-leadership can you identify in this movie?

Chariots of Fire (1981) |

In this dramatic film, two athletes compete in the 1924 Summer Olympics. Based on the true story of Eric Liddell, a devout Christian who races to please God and Harold Abrahams, a Jewish student who sprints to overcome prejudice.

How do Eric and Harold balance their individual desires for excellence with a spirit of teamwork?

What other aspects of servant-leadership can you identify in this movie?

Harry Potter (film series) |
(2001-2011)

Based on the novels written by J.K. Rowling, these films tell the story of an orphaned boy, Harry Potter, who is raised by his unkind aunt and uncle until age eleven when he is summoned to Hogwarts School of Witchcraft and Wizadry. While at school, Harry becomes friends with Hermione Granger and Ron Weasley. Throughout the films, Harry and his friends struggle to overcome a powerful and dangerous dark wizard, Lord Voldemort.

How does the trio of friends share leadership while defeating Voldemort?

What other aspects of servant-leadership can you identify in this movie?

Herb and Dorothy (2008) |

This documentary, directed by Megumi Sasaki, tells the story of a middle class couple, Herb, a USPS mail clerk, and Dorothy, a librarian, who amass one of the world's largest and important modern art collections.

What does this movie say about the challenges of finding a balance as you pursue your passion?

What other aspects of servant-leadership can you identify in this movie?

As with movies, we can find examples of servant-leadership and servant-leaders in many of the books, newspapers and magazines we read.

Here we share with you examples to trigger your watching for such illustrations of servant-leadership as you do your own reading. Such an activity can be illuminating for your personal development as a servant-leader and form the foundation for rewarding conversations with others. Here the quotations are identified according to category. You will notice that these quotations are primarily from the Victorian period, which is characterized by a particularly intimate writing style. With attention to body language, the inner psyche and dynamics between people, authors in that era powerfully described many of the aspects involved in servant-leadership covered in the workbook.

W]hat the world stigmatizes as romantic is often more nearly allied to the truth than is commonly supposed … .

Ann Brontë, *The Tenant of Wildfell Hall*

[She] felt that she was understood partly, and wished to be understood further; for however old, plain, humble, desolate, afflicted we may be, so long as our hearts preserve the feeblest spark of life, they preserve also, shivering near that pale ember, a starved, ghostly longing for appreciation and affection.

Charlotte Brontë, *Shirley*

[I]t seems to me it's the same with love and happiness as with sorrow – the more we know of it the better we can feel what other people's lives are or might be, and so we shall only be more tender to 'em, and wishful to help 'em. The more knowledge a man has the better he'll do his work; and feeling's a sort 'o knowledge.

George Eliot

Adam Bede

Of course, I should often be influenced by my feelings: they were given me to that end.

Charlotte Brontë, *Shirley*

Natural affections and instincts, my dear sir, are the most beautiful of the Almighty's works, but like other beautiful works of His, they must be reared and fostered, or it is as natural that they should be wholly obscured, and that new feelings should usurp their place, as it is that the sweetest productions of the earth, left untended, should be choked with weeds and briers.

Charles Dickens, *The Life and Adventures of Nicholas Nickleby*

Intuition |

[T]he common eye sees only the outside of things, and judges by that; but the seeing eye pierces through and reads the heart and the soul, finding there capacities which the outside didn't indicate or promise, and which the other kind of eye couldn't detect.

Mark Twain, *Personal Recollections of Joan of Arc*

Some feelings are like our hearing: they come as sounds do, before we know their reason.

George Eliot, *Daniel Deronda*

Freedom and Equality |

Pray, who shall judge what we require if not we ourselves? We require simply freedom; we require the lid to be taken off the box in which we have been kept for centuries. You say it's a very comfortable, cozy, convenient box, with nice glass sides, so that we can see out, and that all that's wanted is to give another quiet turn to the key. That is very easily answered. Good gentlemen, you have never been in the box, and you haven't the least idea how it feels!

Henry James, *The Bostonians*

Compassion and peace, in whose service we find perfect freedom.

Katherine Elberfeld

Founder, The Gabriel Center for Servant-Leadership

Personal Awareness |

There is a great deal of unmapped country within us which would have to be taken into account in an explanation of our gusts and storms.

George Eliot, *Daniel Deronda*

'What do you mean, Phib?' asked Miss Squeers, looking in her own little glass, where, like most of us, she saw — not herself, but the reflection of some pleasant image in her own brain.

Charles Dickens, *The Life and Adventures of Nicholas Nickleby*

I know less about myself than about most people in the world ... .

Charles Dickens, *Our Mutual Friend*

Wanting to lead and believing that you can lead are only the departure points on the path to leadership. Leadership is an art, a performing art. And in the art of leadership, the artist's instrument is the self. The mastery of the art of leadership comes with the mastery of self. Ultimately, leadership development is a process of self-development.

James Kouzes and Barry Posner

The Leadership Challenge

Receptiveness is a rare and massive power, like fortitude ... .

George Eliot, *Daniel Deronda*

| *Active Listening*

Community was felt before it was called good.

George Eliot, *Daniel Deronda*

| *Community*

1. THEN was not non-existent nor existent: there was no realm of air, no sky beyond it. What covered in, and where? and what gave shelter? Was water there, unfathomed depth of water?
2. Death was not then, nor was there aught immortal: no sign was there, the day's and night's divider. That One Thing, breathless, breathed by its own nature: apart from it was nothing whatsoever.
3. Darkness there was: at first concealed in darkness this All was indiscriminated chaos. All that existed then was void and form less: by the great power of Warmth was born that Unit.
4. Thereafter rose Desire in the beginning, Desire, the primal seed and germ of Spirit. Sages who searched with their heart's thought discovered the existent's kinship in the non-existent.
5. Transversely was their severing line extended: what was above it then, and what below it? There were begetters, there were mighty forces, free action here and energy up yonder.
6. Who verily knows and who can here declare it, whence it was born and whence comes this creation? The Gods are later than this world's production. Who knows then whence it first came into being?
7. He, the first origin of this creation, whether he formed it all or did not form it, Whose eye controls this world in highest heaven, he verily knows it, or perhaps he knows not.

Rig Veda 10.129

| *Creation and Chaos*

Group Dynamics | Companies thrive when they have dense social networks, high levels of trust, and norms of cooperation. But management theory and practice are full of ways to undercut them. ... Yes, efficiency is important, but not at the cost of the breathing space and time that human connections — and thought — need in order to flourish.

Laurence Prusak, Donald J. Cohen, "How to Invest in Social Capital,"
Harvard Business Review

Meetings | In Japanese there is an expression, *ichigo ichie*, which is mostly associated with the tea ceremony. It means 'one meeting, one life' and refers to the fact that each tea gathering is totally unique. Even if it happened again (for instance, if the same guests were in attendance), the mood, the weather, the placement of the objects in the room — something would be different. Each gathering is a once-in-a-lifetime event.

In a sense, ichigo ichie is the secret of the present moment, because when we are fully awake to the uniqueness of each new situation, we are fully alive. We are responding directly to something fresh and new. And so we should begin and end each meditation (and, The Gabriel Center would add, gathering) with the thought, 'This meeting will never come again.'

Clark Strand, "The Wooden Bowl: Simple Meditation for Everyday Life"
Lent Day by Day 2004, St. Columba's Episcopal Church, Washington, D.C.

Effective Group Climate | 'There is often something poisonous in the air of public rooms,' said Lydgate. 'Strong men (and women) can stand it, but it tells on people in proportion to the delicacy of their systems.'

George Eliot, *Middlemarch*

Disciplined Reflection | Stacy taped two sheets of blank newsprint to the wall ... There was something of the natural teacher in his manner ... He printed rapidly and neatly ... 'What do we have first?' He lifted his marker and looked at us. Like any good instructor, he was going to make sure we supplied most of the answers.

Sue Grafton, *Q is for Quarry*

Decision Making | Clarifying expectations sometimes takes a great deal of courage. It seems easier to act as though differences don't exist and to hope things will work out than it is to face the differences and work together to arrive at a mutually agreeable set of expectations.

Stephen R. Covey, *The 7 Habits of Highly Effective People*

| 179

Their (Emma and two of her friends) being fixed, so absolutely fixed, in the same place was bad for each, for all three. No one of them had the power of removal or of effecting any material change of society. They must encounter each other and make the best of it.

Jane Austen, *Emma*

The Changs (tennis pro Michael Chang's family) were living out an American dream that even most Americans had forgotten, but their extraordinary closeness would make them the objects of suspicion and snide criticisms in the world of junior tennis and even later on the pro tour.

The criticism we've tended to get was always based on a misunderstanding of our Asian concept of family bonding,' Michael told me ... One of the key issues is the role of the father. He just isn't the supreme authority in a Chinese family, so you don't get some of the stresses and tensions that that situation creates. Most people find it surprising, but Asian families don't have nearly the same hierarchy of authority. We tend to put more emphasis on group discussion, and our decisions are more collective. When it works that way, there's less motivation or need to rebel.'

Peter Bodo, *The Courts of Babylon*

[T]he real engine of human endeavor is a genetically programmed preference for collaboration over competition. As the human species emerged, we began to collaborate in specialities like hunting and gathering, which in turn created societies, communities of mutual care.

Bennett J. Sims, *Servanthood: Leadership for the Third Millenium*

| *Decision Making*

Every exercise of power incorporates a faint, almost imperceptible, element of contempt for those over whom the power is exercised. One can only dominate another human soul if one knows, understands, and with the utmost tact despises the person one is subjugating.

Sándor Márai, *Embers*

| *Power*

In a school carried on by sheer cruelty ... there is not likely to be much learnt.

Charles Dickens, *David Copperfield*

In five days the only toxins Anna had sniffed came from the head waitress, Tiny Bigalo, a dried-up wisp of a woman with the energy of a hundred monkeys, all of which, if put in a barrel, would be no fun. According to her staff, Tiny, autocratic by habit and inclination, had ... 'a burr under her saddle' or 'been on a tear for weeks.' As a consequence, everyone associated with the dining room scurried about in tight-lipped resentment expressing their frustrations by clashing dishes and slopping coffee.

Nevada Barr, High Country

Coercion is pressure. 'Do as I say, think as I do, speak as I wish — or else!' Manipulation is the process of guiding people into beliefs or actions that they do not fully understand and that may or may not be good for them. Persuasion involves (the one being persuaded) arriving at a feeling of rightness about a belief or action through one's own intuitive sense ... Persuasion is usually a slow, deliberate, and painstaking process. And sometimes, in the process of persuading, one must endure a wrong or an injustice longer than one thinks one should.

Robert K. Greenleaf, On Becoming a Servant Leader

Servant power functions as a two-way exchange, never as subjugating dominance; it not only influences others, but is also open to influence. Servanthood acknowledges and respects the freedom of another and seeks to enhance the other's capacity to make a difference. Wherever such leadership is exercised — at home, at work, in business and ... (faith communities), in the classroom and throughout the globe — it can result in an astonishing increase in zest, creativity, productivity and, best of all, in bonding people into communities of caring. This is the 'velvet and steel'of servant leadership, a mystical blend of gentleness and strength. It is a paradox that gains by giving.

Bennett J. Sims, Servanthood: Leadership for the Third Millenium

We hope you enjoy looking through these quotations and discovering more in your own reading.

going forward

MAKING PLANS |

In working toward any goal, it is essential to have a plan. We encourage you to use the following questions in developing a plan to continue your servant-leader journey. We also invite you to choose a partner with whom to share the journey and to be accountable to each other in holding to your plans.

Course of Action for Individuals

The following questions are to be used as you chart your personal journey and begin to tap into your intuition and foresight.

Where am I at this stage of my life?

What destinations do I want to experience?

Why am I making the journey?

What baggage do I need to leave by the wayside?

What do I need to pick up instead?

To whom should I listen on the journey?

What signposts do I tend to ignore?

Which skills do I want to pick up along the way?

How will I celebrate and enjoy the trip?

Can I claim any useful symbols as my own guides?

What are the gifts and talents that I bring on the journey?

What are my gifts and talents as others see them?

What concept or practice do I plan to use within the next week?

What three steps will I take in the next six months to further my servant-leader journey?

How will I be a servant-leader to myself, my family, my friends?

How will I be a servant-leader to my colleagues?

How will I be a servant-leader in my community?

Use the following questions to chart your organizational journey.

Where are we now with mission, values, vision?

Where do we want to go?

Why are we making the trip?

To whom should we listen on the journey?

How can we introduce servant-leadership?

What strategies and policies should change?

How can we celebrate and enjoy the trip?

Can we claim any symbols as guides?

Note: If employees from the same organization are present, they may wish to team up for this exercise.

Leadership happens everywhere. It can be a full-time professional role, a consulting or training position or helping to facilitate a team in a setting such as your volunteer work, faith community or family life. As you begin your work either individually or as a member of a facilitation team, the following are **guidelines and suggestions for successful engagements**:

- Servant-leadership is group-centered rather than teacher- or authority-centered. The learners' needs are central.
- We model what we ask of others, whether it is our clients or participants in other kinds of groups.
- Servant-leadership is a process and a lifelong journey. Our role is to learn and to support, model and guide others in their process of exploration.
- Servant-leaders place a high value on creating and sustaining ongoing relationships.
- When working as a facilitation team, servant-leaders exhibit shared leadership in delivery and design.
- Prior to the event, servant-leaders "get on board" with each other. They share the perspectives and experiences they bring to their task, any events that could have an impact on their work together and identify issues that could affect their productivity as facilitators.
- When consulting, proper and adequate planning ensures successful engagements. Always allow enough planning time for yourself and others involved.
- Have a back-up plan for emergencies.
- Reflection upon experience is a core component of group functions and consulting engagements. Ample time is always incorporated to allow participants to reflect upon their experiences and learnings in a particular event.
- When consulting, learn about your clients, including their goals and objectives.
- Exhibit enthusiastic and authentic delivery skills.
- Incorporate adult learning theory into your design and programs when appropriate. Remember and be sensitive to various learning styles and behavior attributes when training.
- Start and end on time if you are running a program or facilitating a meeting.

• Conduct an evaluation process whether you are delivering a program or training or working with others to perform a task or deliver a joint program. If there are time constraints, you may conduct an informal "How did we do?" using a "Plus and Delta" process, or lead an E-I-A-G on an experience that a group member recalls as having had a significant effect on what happened.

• Drawing learnings is critical for individual and group learning. There are several layers of evaluation:

   a) First, evaluate the event yourself. What were your learnings? What worked well? What can be improved? What are applications for the future?

   b) If you are a member of a facilitation team, conduct an evaluation with your partner(s).

   c) And always debrief the engagement with the client.

Organizational transformation is always difficult. Yet one of the key skills of a servant-leader is to nurture change even though it is not easy. Many who have introduced servant-leadership into organizations have followed the model of Robert Greenleaf at AT&T, who used the following strategies:

• Try to "live the change" first in one's own behavior.
• Spend time developing support for the idea before introducing it.
• If others think the idea is theirs, so much the better.
• Stay under the radar at first, with patience.

Again, encourage freedom of expression without forcing anyone to share his or her journey.

We wish you success on your journey toward becoming a servant-leader.

Let the torch of visible community be lit.

George Eliot, *Daniel Deronda*

acknowledgements

Becoming a Servant-Leader represents what can be achieved in a collaborative servant-leader effort. The vision of the Gabriel Center for Servant-Leadership is to bring forward and continue the rich history and knowledge of the Mid-Atlantic Training Consultants (MATC) and the numerous individuals who have contributed to nurturing a servant-led culture in individuals and organizations. For their wisdom and knowledge, we are grateful. The recent evolution of this work would not have been possible without the generous support of Catherine and James Fort. The Forts dedicated their lives to servant-leader initiatives throughout the world and were guiding forces in the development of the Gabriel Center.

Over the years the project team of Natalie Abruzzo, Haris Aqil, Jackie Bahn-Henkelman, Angela Churchill, Katherine Elberfeld, Mark Elberfeld, Nathaniel Elberfeld, Kenneth Fockele, Donald Frick, Kathleen Giles, Janet Graham, Claudia Goetschi, Jan Day Gravel, Kevin Grierson, Amanda Harris, Jim Henkelman-Bahn, Heather Clauson Haughian, Brett Johnson, Rayna Schroeder, Lauren Stanley, Johnny Vardeman, Alexandra Waller and LuAnne Wohler contributed their knowledge, experiences and lessons learned to create a resource useful to all who strive to integrate servant-leadership into their lives and organizations.

Our hope is that you will build upon the work brought forth here and share your knowledge to foster the capacities in others whose lives you touch every day.

about the authors

Rayna Schroeder |

Facilitate is the word that best describes what Rayna does for her clients as a life and leadership coach, management consultant, and trainer. Facilitate is defined as "making progress easier," and she has been doing it her whole life. Born to deaf parents, Rayna acted as interpreter and link to the hearing world, making things easier for them. As a volunteer high school coach, she developed a coaching style that tapped into the creativity and leadership of each individual and taught the values of teamwork and believing in yourself.

Early in her high school coaching and her career as an employee with the Department of Energy, Rayna modeled the leadership style she had experienced growing up. Leaders yelled, controlled and dictated — and she was good at it. Then she began to notice that while she had people doing what she wanted them to do, their hearts were not in it, and they were not growing and learning. Rayna studied other leadership styles and saw how those who listened inspired a shared vision, built relationships and committed themselves to the growth and development of themselves and others were the true leaders. She then adopted the style of servant-leadership before ever knowing it had a name and made helping others grow and develop her personal mission.

Rayna has worked with executives and leaders at all levels delivering coaching for individual and organizational effectiveness, designing and delivering leadership training and development programs, and designing and implementing change initiatives. As CEO, Chief Encouragement Officer, of Joy of Life Coaching, Rayna focuses on the best in others and enables her clients to see the best in themselves. She builds highly personalized partnerships that help her clients identify and use their strengths, be more engaged and build engagement in others, and flourish and thrive at work, not just survive.

Rayna is a former board member and board chairperson of the Servant-Leader Development Center (now The Gabriel Center for Servant-Leadership), formerly located in Alexandria, Virginia.

Rayna holds a Bachelor's degree in Business and Management from the University of Maryland, a Master's degree in Positive Psychology from the American Graduate University of Positive Psychology and is a Professional Certified Coach (PCC) through the International Coach Federation (ICF). She is certified in a wide variety of assessments and 360 degree instruments. Rayna lives Northwest of Baltimore in Eldersburg, Maryland with her wonderful husband Gary and their two cats, Perry (Mason) and Della (Street).

Jim Henkelman-Bahn is a principal in Bahn-Henkelman Consultants. He practices as an independent consultant in organization development, leadership development and diversity management. Much of his work in recent years has been in developing countries working through United Nations agencies. While his practice includes both nonprofit as well as for-profit organizations and agencies, more focus has been with nonprofit organizations, including educational and faith-based organizations.

| Jim Henkelman-Bahn, Ph.D

Jim has his doctorate from Harvard University and a master's degree in Applied Behavioral Sciences from Whitworth College. During his career on the faculty of the University of Maryland College Park, he initiated and directed an experiential doctoral program in Human Resource Development. He is currently an Emeritus Associate Professor in the College of Education at the University of Maryland. After retiring from the University of Maryland College Park, Jim joined his wife and partner, Jackie, in working with countries of the developing world through the United Nations. He has also been a member of the faculty of the Cleveland State University Master's Degree, Diversity Management Program, offered in collaboration with the NTL Institute for Applied Behavioral Sciences. He is an emeritus member of he NTL Institute, where he has been co-steward of the Diversity/Inclusion/Social Justice Community of Practice.

Recently Jim has worked with and been a board member

for a nonprofit organization in his community of Silver Spring, Maryland, to develop leadership for diverse grassroots existing and potential leaders. The organization, IMPACT Silver Spring, envisions a community of empowered peoples where all have a full voice in this demographically changing inner suburb of Washington, DC. He is also a founding member of the Center for Emotional Intelligence and Human Relations Skills where he was chair of the Board of Directors of the Center.

Jim and Jackie live in Silver Spring, Maryland, centrally located among their four children and their families.

Jacqueline Bahn- | Henkelman, Ph.D

Dr. Bahn-Henkelman is a principal in Bahn-Henkelman Consultants. Jackie has always been interested in helping people and organizations improve their effectiveness. That ranged from being a protective service worker for elderly, followed by being a psychotherapist, to working with individuals and teams from United Nations Agencies around the world.

When asked to be the interim executive director for the "Servant Leader Center" in the late 1990's it felt like a good fit. She brought her varied skills to the task and became an ardent admirer and enthusiast of the concept.

Jackie has been instrumental in the start-up of several non-profit organizations:

Opportunities Associates (Romania) An organization that was created in the early 1990's to teach leadership and socially responsibility skills to individuals being prepared to lead the newly formed social service agencies following the end of the Nicolae Ceausescu's reign.

IMPACT Silver Spring (Maryland) was also formed in the early 1990's, was created to develop grass root leaders to better reflect the newly reorganized community and its population.

Emotional Intelligence (EQ) and Human Relations (HR) Skills Center was created in 2007. The Center was created to serve faith-based leaders. It offers the unique combination of a comprehensive **Emotional Intelligence** assessment (an inventory completed by the individual and up to 20 others) that is then used by the individual as he/she participates in a 5-day workshop exploring his or her EQ and HR sills. Jackie is one of the founding board members, led the first program committee and is now the Chair of the Board.

She is a member of NTL where she is both a Human Relations Trainer and a Coach. She is also a coach for students in the American University Masters in Organization Development program and a trainer and a coach in the EQ-HR Center.

Jackie is aware that she saw servant-leadership in action early in life as the daughter of two generous and loving parents. She lives with her partner-spouse Jim Henkelman-Bahn in Silver Spring, Maryland and is lucky enough to have all of their four children and their families within two hours driving distance of their home.

photography credits

40   Norwegian fjord; Katherine Elberfeld. Used by permission.

40   Cahokia mounds, Collinsville, Ill.; Katherine Elberfeld. Used by permission.

40   Japanese garden, Portland, Ore.; Katherine Elberfeld. Used by permission.

41   Stairs at Montserrat, Spain; Mark Elberfeld. Used by permission.

41   Lighted candles in abbey basilica, Montserrat, Spain; Mark Elberfeld. Used by permission.

41   Clock at Musée d'Orsay, Paris, France. Katherine Elberfeld. Used by permission.

56   Peruvian couple; from Passion of Peru, A Photographic Essay; William M. Galardi; Carpe Diem Publishers, Ltd.; Gainesville, Ga.; 2002; used by permission.

56   Zen garden, Portland, Ore; Katherine Elberfeld. Used by permission.

57   Sparks; Katherine Elberfeld. Used by permission.

57   Mexican statue; Alexandra Waller. Used by permission.

112   Arc de Triomphe; Paris, France; Katherine Elberfeld.

112   Eiffel Tower; Paris, France; Katherine Elberfeld.

112   The Biltmore Estate, Asheville, N.C.; Katherine Elberfeld. Used by permission.

112   Nativity, Sculpture at La Sagrada Familia by Antoni Gaudi; Barcelona, Spain; Katherine Elberfeld. Used by permission.

113   Chimneys; Casa Mila, apartment house designed by Antoni Gaudi; Barcelona, Spain; Mark Elberfeld. Used by permission.

113   Hands; Mark Elberfeld. Used by permission.

113   Desert blossom, outside Tuscon, Ariz.; Katherine Elberfeld.

Used by permission.

113   Pueblo Indian rain pot; Katherine Elberfeld. Used by permission.

119   Baxter State Park, Maine; Mark Fockele. Used by permission.

119   Whitewater; Bureau of Land Management. Produced by U.S. Government. Public domain.

138   Wilma Mankiller received the Presidential Medal of Freedom from President Bill Clinton in 1998; David Cornsilk. Produced by U.S. Government. Public domain.

138   Mother Teresa received the Presidential Medal of Freedom from President Ronald Reagan in 1985; photographer unknown. Produced by U.S. Government. Public Domain.

138   Princess Diana at the White House. Produced by U.S. Government. Public Domain.

138   Queen Kaahumanu; artist unknown.

139   Mohandas Gandhi, 1931; photographer unknown. Public domain.

141   President Nelson Mandela; Produced by U.S. Government. Public Domain.

142   Archbishop Desmond Tutu; Benny Gool. Released by photographer and subject into the public domain.

142   Millard and Linda Fuller built houses in Shreveport, La., in 2006. Photo courtesy of the Fuller Center.

144   Maasai women and children, October 2006; Steve Pastor. Released by photographer into the public domain.

170   Ceiling, La Sagrada Familia by Antoni Gaudi; Barcelona, Spain; Katherine Elberfeld. Used by permission.

170   Building detail, Prague, The Czech Republic; Katherine Elberfeld. Used by permission.

170   Statue of Freedom, fashioned from a Soviet statue, Budapest, Hungary; Katherine Elberfeld. Used by permission.

171   Pyramid, Giza, Egypt; Mark Elberfeld. Used by permission.

171   Russian dolls for sale at a market, Moscow, Russia; Mark Elberfeld. Used by permission.

188   Street celebration, Milan, Italy; Mark Elberfeld. Used by permission.

references

xiii   Nye, Joseph S., Jr., "A Dollop of Deeper American Values: Why 'Soft Power' Matters in Fighting Terrorism," Washington, DC: *The Washington Post*, 2004.

xiii   Fisher, Roger, and William Ury, *Getting to Yes: Negotiating Agreement Without Giving In*: Boston: Houghton Mifflin/Trade & Reference, 1991. Used by permission.

21   "The Johari Window: A Graphic Model of Awareness in Interpersonal Relationship" by Joseph Luft, *Reading Book for Human Relations Trainings*, 8th Edition, 1999

29   Goleman, Daniel, *Working With Emotional Intelligence*, New York: Random House, Inc., 2000.

29   Chapman, Margaret, *Emotional Intelligence Pocketbook*, Herndon: Management Pocketbooks, 2005. Used by permission.

31   Goleman, Daniel, "What Makes a Leader," Watertown: *Harvard Business Review*, 1998.

40   Carpenter, Edward, "The Lake of Beauty," *A New Zealand Prayer Book*: Harper Collins Book, 1989.

40   Eliot, George, *Daniel Deronda*, 1876, Project Gutenberg, Accessed July 7, 2008, http://www.gutenberg.org/dirs/etext05/8drda10.txt. Public domain.

41   Goleman, Daniel et al., *Primal Leadership*, Boston: Harvard Business School Publishing, 2002. Used by permission.

41   Dickens, Charles, *David Copperfield*, New York: Random House, Inc., 1992. Used by permission.

46   "Now Hear This and Pay Attention" by Don Oldenburg. *The Washington Post*, Tuesday, February 20, 2001: Page C04

56   Mother Teresa, *The Joy in Loving*, New Delhi: Penguin Books

India, 1996.

56   Petras, Kathryn, and Ross Petras, *The Whole World Book of Quotations*: New York: Addison-Wesley Publishing Co., 1995.

57   Eliot, George, *Middlemarch*, New York: Random House, Inc., 1985. Used by permission.

61   American Heritage Dictionary of the English Language, 4th edition, Boston: Houghton Mifflin, 2000.

62   Gibb, Jack R., and Leland P. Bradford, Kenneth Benne, Gibb Trust Formation Theory of Group Development: *Working Effectively in Groups and Teams, A MATC Resource Book*, 1991.

69   Covey, Stephen R., *The 7 Habits of Highly Effective People*, New York: Simon & Schuster, 1989.

75   Hagberg, Janet, *Real Power: Stages of Personal Power*, Salem: Sheffield Publishing Co., 2003. Used by permission.

75   Benne, Kenneth D., and Paul Sheats, *Theories and Models in Applied Behavioral Science Vol. 2 group*, San Diego: Pfeiffer & Co., 1991. Used by permission.

112   Hugo, Victor, *Les Misérables*, New York: Penguin Group (USA), Inc., 1987. Used by permission.

112   Wheatley, Margaret, *Leadership and the New Science: Discovering Order in a Chaotic World*, San Francisco: Berrett-Koehler Publishers, 1999, p. XX. Used by permission.

112   *Napoleon inconnu (1786-1793)*, Frederic Masson and Guido Biagi, eds. Paris: Ollendorff, 1895. Vol. 1, pg. 155

113   Sims, Bennett J., *Servanthood: Leadership for the Third Millenium*, Boston: Cowley Publications, 1997. Used by permission.

113   Paterson, Katherine, *Words of Women, Quotations for Success*, Power Dynamics Publishing, 1997.

121   Olson, Edwin, Glenda H. Eoyang, Richard Beckhard, and Peter Vaill, *Facilitating Organization Change: Lessons from Complexity Science*, San Francisco: Jossey-Bass/Pfeiffer, 2001. Used by permission.

122   Olson, Edwin, Glenda H. Eoyang, Richard Beckhard, and Peter Vaill, *Facilitating Organization Change: Lessons from Complexity Science*, San Francisco: Jossey-Bass/Pfeiffer, 2001. Used by permission.

127   Johnson, Barry, "Polarity Management: Identifying and Managing Unsolvable Problems," Amherst, MA: HRD Press, 1992

127   Oswald, Roy M. and Johnson, Barry, *Managing Polarities in*

Congregations: Eight Keys for Thriving Faith Communities, The Alban Institute, 2009. Additional information is available at the website: www.polaritymanagement.com. Used by permission.

135   Covey, Steven, "The Three Roles of the Leader in the New Paradigm," in *The Leader of the Future: New Visions, Strategies, and Practices for the Next Era*, 1996.

135   Collins, Jim, *Good to Great*, New York: Harper Collins, 2001. Used by permission.

136   SanFacon, George, "Awake at Work, Concepts and Principles for Creating Better Workplaces and a Better World," University of Michigan, Ann Arbor, 2004, Accessed June 7, 2008, http://www.housing.umich.edu/pdfs/fac_awake-at-work.pdf. Used by permission.

137   Lamott, Anne, *Plan B: Further Thoughts on Faith*, New York: Riverhead Books, 2005, p. 303

139   Gandhi, Mohandas, *Nonviolence in Peace and War*, Vol. 1, Ahmedabad, India: Navajivan Pub. House, 1942.

140   Roy, Amit, "Churchill was willing to let Gandhi starve," *The Telegraph*, Calcutta, India, Jan. 2, 2006, Accessed June 9, 2008. http://www.telegraphindia.com/1060102/asp/nation/story_5670718.asp

141   "Not honouring Gandhi was a mistake: Nobel Foundation," *The Tribune*, Chandigarh, India, Oct. 3, 2007, Accessed June 9, 2008. http://www.tribuneindia.com/2007/20071003/main3.htm.

141   Mandela, Nelson, Address to the conference Peace, Nonviolence and Empowerment: Gandhian Philosophy in the 21st Century, New Delhi, India, Jan. 29, 2007, Accessed June 9, 2008, Recording available at http://www.satyagrahaconference.com/confpapers.asp.

143   One-time permission to reprint quotation from Bren Dubay granted by Koinonia Farm on Aug. 18, 2008. For further information about Koinonia and/or Clarence Jordan, please visit www.koinoniapartners.org, write to 1324 Ga. Hwy. 49 S, Americus, Ga. 31719, or call (229) 924-0391. Visitors welcomed year round.

144   Scherer, John, Scherer Leadership Center Maasai Newsletters, 2005, Accessed July 30, 2008, http://www.scherercenter.com/?page_id=97. Used by permission.

146   Scherer, John, Scherer Leadership Center Maasai Newsletters, 2005, Accessed July 30, 2008, http://www.scherercenter.com/?page_id=97. Used by permission.

149 University of Michigan Housing Facilities Website, Accessed June 7, 2008, http://www.housing.umich.edu/services/facilities/general.html. Used by permission.

150 SanFacon, George, "Awake at Work, Concepts and Principles for Creating Better Workplaces and a Better World," University of Michigan, Ann Arbor, 2004, Accessed June 7, 2008, http://www.housing.umich.edu/pdfs/fac_awake-at-work.pdf. Used by permission.

152 Gimbel, Barney, "Southwest's New Flight Plan," *Fortune*, May 16, 2005, Accessed June 7, 2008. http://money.cnn.com/magazines/fortune/fortune_archive/2005/05/16/8260158/index.htm

152 Southwest Airlines Website, Accessed June 7, 2008, www.southwest.com. Used by permission.

155 Spector, Robert, *The Nordstrom Way: The Inside Story of America's #1 Customer Service Company*, New York: John Wiley & Sons, 1995. Used by permission.

158 TDIndustries Website, Accessed June 7, 2008, www.tdindustries.com. Used by permission.

159 TDIndustries Website, Accessed June 7, 2008, www.tdindustries.com. Used by permission.

170 Eliot, George, *Daniel Deronda*, 1876, Project Gutenberg, Accessed July 7, 2008, http://www.gutenberg.org/dirs/etext05/8drda10.txt. Public domain.

171 Melville, Herman, *Moby-Dick, or, the White Whale*, 1851, Project Gutenberg, Accessed Sept. 15, 2008, http://www.gutenberg.org/dirs/etext01/moby10b.txt Public domain.

171 Twain, Mark, *Personal Recollections of Joan of Arc, by the Sieur Louis de Conte*, 1896. Internet History Sourcebooks Project, Fordham University. 7 Jul. 2008. http://www.fordham.edu/halsall/basis/conte-joanofarc.html. Public domain.

171 Márquez, Gabriel García, *Love in the Time of Cholera*, trans. Edith Grossman, New York: Vintage International, 1988, 2003, p. 165.

176 Brontë, Ann, *The Tenant of Wildfell Hall*, 1848. Project Gutenberg. 12 Jun. 2008. http://www.gutenberg.org/dirs/etext97/wldfl10.txt. Public domain.

176 Brontë, Charlotte, *Shirley*, 1849. Nagoya University, Japan. 7 Jul. 2008. http://www.lang.nagoya-u.ac.jp/~matsuoka/Bronte-Shirley.html. Public domain.

176 Eliot, George, *Adam Bede*, New York: Random House, Inc.,

2000. Used by permission.

176 Brontë, Charlotte, *Shirley*, 1849. Nagoya University, Japan. 7 Jul. 2008. http://www.lang.nagoya-u.ac.jp/~matsuoka/Bronte-Shirley.html. Public domain.

177 Dickens, Charles, *The Life and Adventures of Nicholas Nickleby*, 1839. Project Gutenberg. 7 Jul. 2008. http://www.gutenberg.org/files/967/967-h/967-h.htm. Public domain.

177 Twain, Mark, *Personal Recollections of Joan of Arc, by the Sieur Louis de Conte*, 1896. Internet History Sourcebooks Project, Fordham University. 7 Jul. 2008. http://www.fordham.edu/halsall/basis/conte-joanofarc.html. Public domain.

177 Eliot, George, *Daniel Deronda*, 1876, Project Gutenberg, Accessed July 7, 2008, http://www.gutenberg.org/dirs/etext05/8drda10.txt. Public domain.

177 James, Henry, *The Bostonians*, 1886. Project Gutenberg. 7 Jul. 2008. http://www.gutenberg.org/files/19718/19718-h/19718-h.htm. Public domain.

177 Eliot, George, *Daniel Deronda*, 1876, Project Gutenberg, Accessed July 7, 2008, http://www.gutenberg.org/dirs/etext05/8drda10.txt. Public domain.

177 Dickens, Charles, *The Life and Adventures of Nicholas Nickleby*, 1839. Project Gutenberg. 7 Jul. 2008. http://www.gutenberg.org/files/967/967-h/967-h.htm. Public domain.

178 Dickens, Charles, *Our Mutual Friend*, 1865. Project Gutenberg. 7 Jul. 2008. http://www.gutenberg.org/files/883/883-h/883-h.htm. Public domain.

178 Eliot, George, *Daniel Deronda*, 1876, Project Gutenberg, Accessed July 7, 2008, http://www.gutenberg.org/dirs/etext05/8drda10.txt. Public domain.

178 Eliot, George, *Daniel Deronda*, 1876, Project Gutenberg, Accessed July 7, 2008, http://www.gutenberg.org/dirs/etext05/8drda10.txt. Public domain.

178 "Rig Veda" 10.129, Trans. Ralph T.H. Griffith. 1896. Sacred-texts.com. 8 Jul. 2008. http://www.sacred-texts.com/hin/rigveda/rv10129.htm. Public domain.

179 Prusak, Laurence, Cohen, Donald J., "How to Invest in Social Capital," in *Harvard Business Review*," June 2001, p. 89. Used by permission.

179 Strand, Clark, *The Wooden Bowl: Simple Meditation for*

Everyday Life.

179   Eliot, George, *Middlemarch*, New York: Random House, Inc., 1985. Used by permission.

179   Grafton, Sue, *Q is for Quarry*, New York: Penguin Group (USA), Inc., 2002. Used by permission.

179   Covey, Stephen R., *The 7 Habits of Highly Effective People*, New York: Simon & Schuster, 1989. Used by permission.

180   Austen, Jane, *Emma*, New York: New American Library, 1989.

180   Bodo, Peter, *The Courts of Babylon*, New York: Carol Mann Agency, 1999. Used by permission.

180   Eliot, George, *Middlemarch*, New York: Random House, Inc., 1985. Used by permission.

180   Sims, Bennett J., *Servanthood: Leadership for the Third Millenium*, Boston: Cowley Publications, 1997. Used by permission.

180   Márai, Sándor, *Embers*, New York: Random House, Inc., 2001. Used by permission.

180   Dickens, Charles, *David Copperfield*, New York: Random House, Inc., 1992. Used by permission.

181   Barr, Nevada, *High Country*, New York: Penguin Group (USA), Inc., 2004. Used by permission.

181   Greenleaf, Robert K., *On Becoming a Servant-Leader*, Hoboken: Wiley Publications, 1996. Used by permission.

181   Sims, Bennett J., *Servanthood: Leadership for the Third Millenium*, Boston: Cowley Publications, 1997. Used by permission.

Also by the Gabriel Center for Servant-Leadership:

To Speak of Love:

Reflections on Servant-Leadership in Life and Work

In the Midst of Sunflowers:

Embracing the Power of the Spirit in Our Life and Work

Green by Design:

A Photo Essay About Servant-Leadership and Nature